F-16 Fighting Falcon
in action

by Lou Drendel

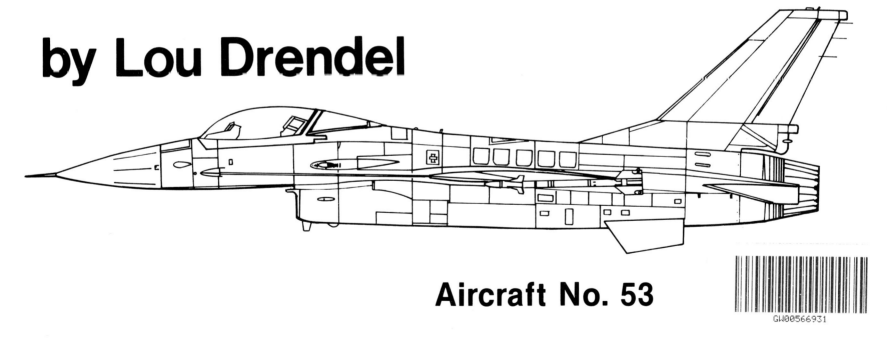

Aircraft No. 53

squadron/signal publications

An F-16A of the 4th TFS, 388 TFW, in the Wing Commander's colors, that was adorned with the Fighting Falcon insignia for the Official Christening Ceremony.

1115 CROWLEY DRIVE, CARROLLTON,TEXAS 75011-5010

ISBN 0-89747-133-4

If you have any photographs of the aircraft, armor, soldiers or ships of any nation, particularly wartime snapshots, why not share them with us and help make Squadron/Signal's books all the more interesting and complete in the future. Any photograph sent to us will be copied and the original returned. The donor will be fully credited for any photos used. Please indicate if you wish us not to return the photos. Please send them to: Squadron/Signal Publications, Inc., 1115 Crowley Dr., Carrollton, TX 75011-5010.

PHOTO CREDITS

USAF
General Dynamics
SSgt. Roy Chismar
Norman E. Taylor
Michael Klaver
Dave Mason
D. VerDoodt
K. Minert
Dr. Carl Eddy
H. Scharringa
Dave Menard

The first operational F-16 unit was the 388th TFW, which was tasked with training the first operational F-16 pilots for USAF and NATO. Each of the 388th's squadron's is represented in this formation, with each aircraft carrying a different ordnance load. (USAF)

INTRODUCTION

In a metaphysical sense, the F-16 can trace it's genealogy to the very first fighters, for it is as close to the ideal fighter as any of the historically great fighter aircraft. It is that rare example of the perfect blend of state-of-the-art and experimental technology, wrapped up in a practical-use package. It is an operational airplane which encompasses some very futuristic design ideas, and keeps them locked within the parameters of current mission tasks. It is what it is because that is exactly what it's creators were commissioned to make it. This is a fact worthy of note, since so many modern combat aircraft have managed to diverge from their stated design goals. The F-16 is notable for being the best clear air mass air-to-air fighter ever designed. The fact that it has also turned out to be one of the best air-to-ground tactical fighters ever designed, without losing any significant air-to-air capability, makes it even more remarkable.

The F-16 grew out of a 1970 directive, to the Navy and Air Force, from Deputy Defense Secretary David Packard, in which he ordered the services to select technologically innovative programs for proof of the 'prototyping concept'. Prototyping was envisioned as a method of making sure that the services would be buying the right weapon, at the right price, by having competing contractors build prototypes that could be tested against each other.

Prototyping ground rules for aircraft were developed by the then Air Force Secretary Robert C. Seamans, Jr. Under these rules, existing force structure was not to be considered a constraint; there would be a minimum of military specification requirements; there would be a minimum of initial performance goals; the systems would be designated 'Y' instead of 'X', since they would contain a mix of current and experimental technologies; a fly-off competition would be held before any decision to go ahead with production was made, though no production commitment was made going into the project; and finally, funding for the program was to be limited: Of the $100 million eventually allocated the lightweight fighter prototype program, General Dynamics got $38 million, Northrop $39 million, and the balance was split between Pratt & Whitney and General Electric, the builders of the LWF engines. This relatively modest sum bought the design, construction, and testing of a pair each of YF-16 and YF-17 aircraft.

The Vietnam War had demonstrated that most modern air combat battles were fought in the transonic zone, from Mach 0.6 to Mach l.6, at medium altitudes. A Mach 2 plus fighter, with all kinds of sophisticated fire control avionics, had it's place in the inventory, but was too expensive to be produced in the numbers that might be necessary to fight a war against an enemy that had numerical superiority to begin with. A small, agile fighter, with rudimentary air-to-air electronics, which could be produced for half the price of it's bigger brothers was a more attractive option. And if it was good for the Air Force, it would also be good for the Navy. This rationale made the lightweight fighter one of the premier candidates for the prototyping experiment. The other candidate was the Advanced Medium STOL Transport (AMST). The AMST was prototyped into the YC-14 and 15 by Boeing and McDonnell Douglas, respectively.

A formal Request For Proposals (RFP) was issued on January 6, 1972, with a deadline for reply of February 18, 1972. Nine companies were invited to submit proposals. Grum-

The first prototype YF-16 was finished in a brilliant Red/White/Blue paint scheme and rolled out of the mammoth (602 acres) Air Force Plant Number 4 at Fort Worth in December, 1973. (General Dynamics)

man, Fairchild, McDonnell Douglas, and Rockwell declined to compete. Proposals were received from LTV, General Dynamics, Boeing, Northrop, and Lockheed. Northrop's proposal was based upon it's P-530 Cobra project, a company-funded effort to find a successor to the F-5. Lockheed's proposal was based upon it's CL-1200 Lancer, which had been envisioned as an updated version of the Starfighter. The other three proposals were based upon entirely new designs. The most important considerations, as far as the Air Force selection board was concerned, were turning radius and acceleration in that transonic zone, and range. Northrop and General Dynamics were named as winners of this competition, and given contracts to build the prototype lightweight fighters.

YF-16 PROTOTYPE

Even though there was no assurance that the lightweight fighter would become a production contract, General Dynamics made the decision to approach their prototype as if it was a production aircraft. They spent lavishly from company funds to production engineer the F-16, and they instructed their foreign sales people to brief friendly foreign air forces on it's potential. There was good reason for this, since several NATO countries were interested in replacing their F-104 Starfighters with a new fighter. While there was some feeling within the USAF that the F-15 Eagle should be sold to our NATO allies, the cost and complexity of the F-15 militated against it's selection by Norway, Denmark, Belgium, and Holland. Their combined need for a new fighter added up to at least 350 aircraft. If the USAF would agree to buy 650 of the new fighters, the price would become competitive enough for the Europeans to consider seriously. In addition to the USAF and NATO markets, there was the U.S. Navy requirement for up to 800 lightweight fighters, and the possibility of sales to several other friendly nations. It all added up to a possible 'sale of the century'.

The first YF-16 was rolled out in December of 1973, just 21 months after contract award. It more than lived up to the officially stated goal of the program, which was to provide the Defense Department with data concerning the benefits of advanced aerodynamic technology to enhance the combat characteristics of the lightweight fighter. The advanced technologies included in the YF-16 design were: Variable-camber wing, Vortex lift, 'Relaxed' static stability, Fly-by-wire control system, Blended wing-body, and a console-mounted control stick. Less radical, but equally important, were the 30 degree tilted seat, and the bubble canopy which allowed the pilot a 360 degree vision.

The YF-16 design allowed great weight savings over more conventional aerodynamic layouts. The use of wing-body blending allowed a fuselage five and a half feet shorter than would have been required without it, and the forebody strakes improved stability and lift at high angle of attack to such a degree that the wing could be cut in size. These two features alone added up to weight savings of over 1,000 pounds. The YF-16 was 81% Aluminum, 4% Steel, 3.7% Titanium, with the balance of the weight in composites. One of the most difficult decisions facing General Dyanmics designers in the intitial stages of design work on the lightweight fighter was the choice between single or twin-engine layouts. There was strong sentiment in some quarters for the added safety of a twin engine airplane, and that is the way Northrop went with their entry into the LWF sweepstakes.

General Dynamics did their homework on this question, just as they had thoroughly researched every other aspect of the lightweight fighter. They discovered that there had been 50 accidents per 100,000 flying hours in singles and 45 per 100,000 hours in twins in 1955. As jet engines increased in reliability, the accident rate went down. The forecast for 1980, when the F-16 would be entering service was 5.3 single and 5.0 twin engine accidents per 100,000 flight hours, Based on that, they concluded that the 15% weight savings offered by the single engine configuration was too good to pass up. After all, they were designing a **lightweight** fighter!

(Top) YF-16s were built for simplified maintenance, with easily removable access panels, and several built in test systems to pinpoint inoperative components. (General Dynamics via D. Verdoodt)

The number two prototype in flight over Edwards AFB in June, 1974. Number two was finished in a camouflage of cloud White and air superiority Blue early in it's career. (USAF)

Keeping the weight down was one thing. Keeping the cost down was another. New technologies, by their very pioneering nature, are often very expensive. Not only was General Dynamics on a fixed budget in the design, construction, and testing of their new fighter, they were also bound to keep the price down if they wanted to sell it. Once again the designers came up with a solution that not only saved money on the initial purchase price, but also simplified maintenance operations. The F-16 uses interchangeable horizontal tails, flaperons, and 80% of the main landing gear parts are also interchangeable from left to right. All flight control servos are the same, and the flaperons and horizontal tails use the same hydraulic ram.

The avionics in the prototypes were kept simple, in keeping with the air superiority mission. They consisted of a General Electric ranging radar system, an Elliot heads-up display, modified for air-to-air use from the air-to-ground system used in the A-7, and a Delco Carousel inertial platform that would feed data points on rate and acceleration into the flight test instrumentation for study by the program managers.

The tricycle landing gear was fuselage mounted, since the wings were far too thin to accomodate the main gear. The nose gear was mounted behind the intake, which prevented debris from being ingested by the engine. With a thrust to weight ratio approaching 1.4 to 1, the YF-16 accelerated briskly enough to make a quick gear retraction necessary to avoid exceeding the 300 knot gear transition limit. Gear retraction was accomplished within 4 seconds.

The test program, like any program to prove a new aircraft, had it's share of exciting moments. In two separate instances, test pilots were forced to make dead-stick landings when contaminants in the fuel control units caused the F-100 engine to go to idle thrust. One landing was made from 15,000 feet, on the USAF pilot's first flight in an F-16, and the other from 1,500 feet, shortly after take-off. In neither case was the aircraft damaged. As the program progressed, it became increasingly evident that the YF-16 was going to rewrite the book on air combat manuevering. It was possible to pull so many Gs, so fast, that the normal G-suit pressure regulator could not keep up, and a newer, faster acting regulator that could inflate the G suits at a rate that could keep up with the airplane's capabilities had to be installed.

In air combat situations against each other, the two YF-16's actually gained altitude. (Most dogfights progress to lower altitudes as the fight occurs.) Starting at 15,000 feet, test pilots generally managed to work the fight up to 30,000 feet. Test pilot Phil Oestricher demonstrated consecutive Immelmann turns, beginning at 5,000 feet and leveling off at 25,000 feet. He indicated that a third Immelmann would have been possible. No fighter then in operational service could have performed such a manuever.

Throughout the entire test program, an extremely high rate of test flights was maintained. In one period 47 flights were flown in 31 days, including 6 flights in one day. This was only possible because of the high degree of reliability of the YF-16's systems. That reliability was made possible by the fact that many of the systems came from operational aircraft, which also enabled General Dynamics to hold down costs. YF-16's used an environmental control system from the A-7, control actuators from the F-111, the nose wheel from the F-4, main gear wheels and tires from the B-58, an air starter from the C-5, and the ejection seat, air data computer, generator drive and engine from the F-15.

These factors, combined with demonstrated performance superiority in acceleration and overall in the transonic drag regime, coupled with lower weight and use of the already proven F-100 engine, which was being used in the F-15, resulted in the USAF decision to buy the F-16. The Navy procrastinated, and eventually opted for a version of the YF-17, the F/A-18.

The USAF decision to buy the F-16 was not helped by it's lower cost. Under the former Secretary of Defense, Robert McNamara, the total force allowed the USAF had been capped at 21 Wings. That meant that the Air Force could only have so many airplanes. The idea, of course, was to hold down spending. But holding down spending in an era of inflationary expectation was next to impossible anyway, and probably only served to cause the Air Force hierarchy to circle the wagons. The accepted way to maintain your influence in a bureaucracy is to maintain your share of the budget. With inflation expanding the budget, there was only one way to do that. The cost of equipment had to go up, and of course, it did.

Secretary of Defense James Schlesinger realized that the 21 wing cap was counter-productive, and allowed the Air Force to add five wings to it's force structure. The reported quid pro quo was that the Air Force buy the F-16. Much of the resistance to an Air Force buy of the lightweight fighter had centered around the theory that it would only be an American Mig-21...small, with good acceleration and turning capability, but short on range and severely limited in diversity. When the performance of the prototypes indicated that the F-16 would exceed the Mig-21 in all categories, with none of it's performance shortcomings, the Air Force did a 180 and began to look forward to adding the F-16 to it's inventory.

Phil Oestricher, General Dynamics Test Pilot, made the first flight of the YF-16. (General Dynamics)

Aerial refuelling test with a KC-135 tanker. The flight evaluation of the prototypes was conducted at Edwards AFB by a joint test team consisting of the contractor, Air Force Systems Command, Air Force Test and Evaluation Center, and Tactical Air Command pilots.

(Above) Number One at the Paris Air Show of 1975. One of it's principle competitors for the "sale of the century", the SAAB Viggen, is in the background (where it remained). (Michel Klaver)

(Top Right) Number Two carried at least three different paint schemes during the flight test program and subsequently. Here it is finished in the same Red/White/Blue scheme as Number One. Worthy of note is the Iranian Flag which adorned test aircraft until 1979. Test equipment included a camera mounted on the deck behind the pilot. (Dave Mason)

(Middle Right) The prototype carried AIM-7E Sparrow missiles underwing for test purposes, but lacked the circuitry to fire them from these stations. (USAF)

(Right) Number Two was also finished in an overall Grey scheme during the test program. Here returning from a mission in which bombs were released from the multiple ejector rack. Note camera under horizontal tail, fitted for these tests. (USAF)

Test of the Sparrow missile on the F-16 was conducted as a result of a chorus of criticism of the F-16's lack of BVR (beyond visual range) capabilities. When the F-16 became the "swing fighter", complimenting, rather than competing with the F-15, the addition of AIM-7 capability was dropped. (General Dynamics)

AIM-7s were also test-carried on the wingtip pylons. (General Dynamics)

Number Two was fitted with pylons on the main gear doors to carry and fire Sparrow Missiles. These tests took place with AIM-7F missiles, in November, 1977. (General Dynamics)

Wheel Door Pylon for AIM 7 Missles

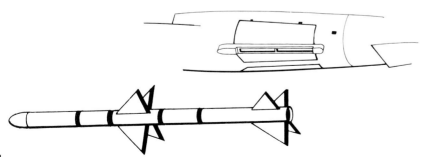

most of these perceived problems had either been anticipated and were in the process of being fixed, or had already been fixed. In spite of this, the GAO issued another critical report exactly one year later, urging complete DOD review of the F-16 program before the Air Force went ahead with it's planned buy of an additional 738 F-16s, which would bring the total USAF buy up to 1,388 aircraft. This report questioned structural integrity, radar operation, flight stability, and implementation of the Foreign Military Sales plan. The Air Force provided point by point rebuttal of the GAO's allegations, and the program continued apace.

In May, 1977 the formal contract was signed with Belgium, Norway, Denmark, and the Netherlands. The same month an F-16 made a non-stop, unrefuelled flight across the United States. In October DOD endorsed full scale production. In February, 1978 the first European assembly line was opened at SONACA/SABCA in Belgium, followed by the second line at Fokker-VFW in the Netherlands. In July the first major European produced components (a set of wings) was attached to a USAF F-16.

In August, tests were conducted with the second prototype YF-16 to prove the viability of delivery of laser guided weapons. The YF-16 consistently scored hits on a 24 foot square target with GBU-10 and GBU-16 laser guided bombs. An Automatic Tracking Laser Illumination System (ATLIS-2) was used in conjunction with a helmet mounted sighting system. It was the first time that laser guided weapons had successfully been delivered from a single seat aircraft. Other milestones that month included the first flight of the first production airplane (78-0001), and the announcement of Israel's intention to procure 75 F-16s.

The first operational F-16A was delivered to the 388th TFW, at Hill AFB, Utah on January 6, 1979. Brigadier General Davis C. Rohr, C.O. of the 388th accepted the aircraft. The 388th was tasked with training the first USAF and foreign F-16 units, and was scheduled to receive 103 F-16s. That same month the Belgian Air Force accepted the first F-16 produced on a European assembly line. The first Dutch assembled aircraft made it's first flight in May.

Other countries were beginning to express interest in the F-16. Canada and Australia were both in the market for a new fighter, and Korea, Greece, and Turkey had all indicated specific interest in the F-16. The thumping success of the F-16's introduction into NATO had provided the right sort of high profile exposure. Lieutenant General Marcel DeSmet, Chief of Staff of the Belgian Air Force, quickly triumphed over a pair of F-104s in ACM on his first flight in the F-16. General DeSmet said that the F-16 "is the 60th type of aircraft I have flown in my pilot career, but truly it is one which gave me the highest satisfaction." The first Dutch pilot to complete the F-16 transition, Captain Bill Snoek, said; "It is an overwhelming experience to fly the F-16!"

The third of the FSD aircraft was finished in this experimental two-tone grey camouflage. (General Dynamics)

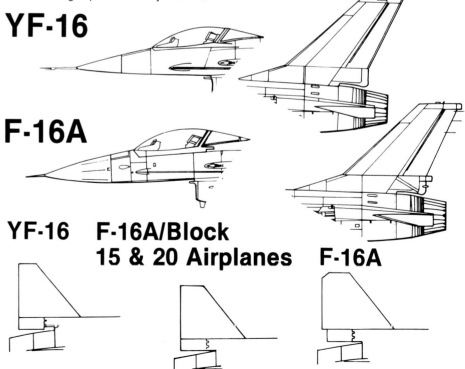

YF-16

F-16A

YF-16   F-16A/Block 15 & 20 Airplanes   F-16A

13

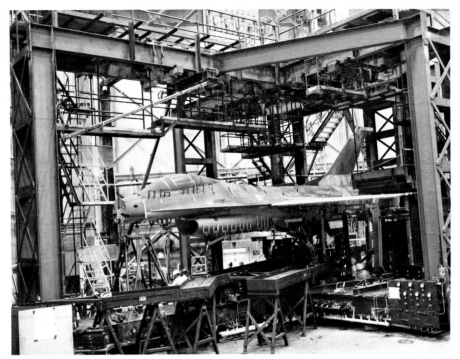

This computer-controlled torture-inducing rig at General Dynamics plant was able to subject a test F-16 airframe to the equivalent of 16,000 flight hours, which is equal to thirty years at the projected rate of usage for the F-16. Thousands of take-offs and landings were simulated, as well as combat maneuvers of up to l0G. Herbert F. Rodgers, Vice President and F-16 Program Director, said: "The test program was particularly successful in identifying specific areas of the airframe that are most susceptible to fatigue. As a result, structural design modifications have been made and tested and will be included in production F-16s." (General Dynamics)

In addition to the highly instrumented nose probe, the FSD test aircraft also carried special cameras under the fuselage to record delivery of underwing ordnance. (USAF)

Unfortunately, everyone within the consortium was not completely happy with the F-16 deal. The Carter Administration, with it's erratic foreign policy, had thrown more than a few monkey wrenches into the third country sales efforts. King Hussein of Jordan had wanted to buy F-16s, but was turned down by Carter. During the Paris Air Show that year, Hussein made sure the F-16 Consortium knew he was considering the Mirage 2000 quite favorably. (They could hardly have failed to have noticed, since the French had parked their 'perfected F-102' in front of the General Dynamics chalet.) Members of the Taiwan Air Force requested orientation flights in the F-16, but the Carter Administration's 'China Card' included a cold shoulder for that China, and they were refused. Korea had also expressed interest in procurement of 80 F-16s, and two of their officers did manage to fly in the F-16, but according to a DOD official at Paris, "Korea couldn't get the time of day from the Carter Administration."

All of these non-sales served to aggravate the NATO consortium, who had counted heavily on them in their decision to buy the F-16. The U.S. ambassador to Belgium, Mrs. Anne Cox Chambers, was in attendance at Paris, and as this debacle unfolded, she attempted to call President Carter. She was fobbed off on Zbigniew Brzezinski, the President's foreign policy advisor, who expressed unrelenting indifference to her complaints.

In spite of these setbacks in the third country sales program, production of the F-16 continued throughout 1979 well ahead of schedule. The Fort Worth line had delivered 74 airplanes as of January, 1980, and the European lines had completed 34 aircraft. The Norwegian Air Force accepted the first of it's 72 F-16s on January 15, 1980, and the Danish Air Force got it's first airplane three days later. The first of the 75 Israeli airplanes had been turned over the previous month. Quality control on the Fort Worth line was the best ever recorded so early in a production program, with 13 of the first 69 airplanes being delivered with zero defects, and a further 31 recording less than five discrepancies. Ease of maintenance which had been designed into the airplane was beginning to show, as Maintenance Man Hours (MMH) per flight hour at Hill AFB dropped steadily towards the stated goal of 19 MMH per flight hour. The operational training unit for the F-16, the 56th TFW at MacDill AFB, Florida, had received the first of their airplanes the previous October.

In the meantime, a moderate mutiny was brewing among USAFE commanders. They worried that the F-16 would be too vulnerable to Soviet fighters with beyond-visual-range (BVR) radars, and were reluctant to accept F-16s if they had to give up their F-4s. (The F-4 was equipped with the BVR Sparrow Missile) The F-16 had demonstrated the ability to fire the Sparrow during the test program, so the primary difficulty was with the relatively simple radar in the F-16. The Air Force promised to look into the possibility of upgrading the radar, as well as testing the General Electric F-101X engine, which had been developed for the B-1. (The F-101 was more powerful than the F-100, and since the B-1 had fallen prey to the Carter axe, it was an engine without an airplane.) Both of these developments greatly disturbed the Consortium, which viewed them as further impediments to their hoped-for third country sales.

Nose Gear

YF-16
Split Doors

F-16A
Single Door

F-16A Cockpit

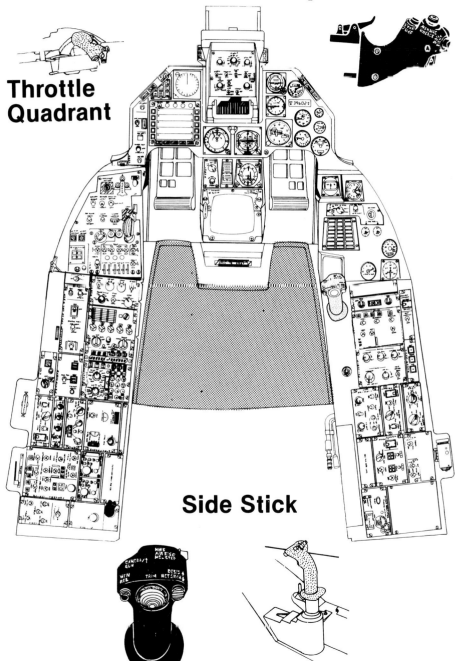

Throttle Quadrant

Side Stick

YF-16 prototype test aircraft instrument panel (top) shows many differences from production operational aircraft instrument panel. (below) Special test instrumentation was outlined in red on instrument panel. (Dave Mason)

The first production F-16A, serial number 78-0001, was completed and accepted by Major General James A. Abrahamson, Air Force F-16 Program Director, on August 17, 1978. (General Dynamics)

Accessibility of components makes maintenance of the F-16 much easier and has contributed to it's besting the F-4's Maintenance Man Hours per flight hour by double. This is the third FSD aircraft, with the SIIIS Seat, not used in production aircraft. (General Dynamics)

Comparison of External Dimensions

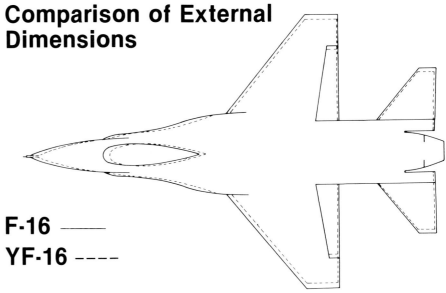

F-16 ———
YF-16 - - - -

F-16 poses with the impressive array of armaments it is able to deliver, including everything from napalm to nukes. The latest production version of the F-16 is able to carry up to 12,000 pounds of ordnance, on nine external stores stations, including wingtips. (General Dynamics)

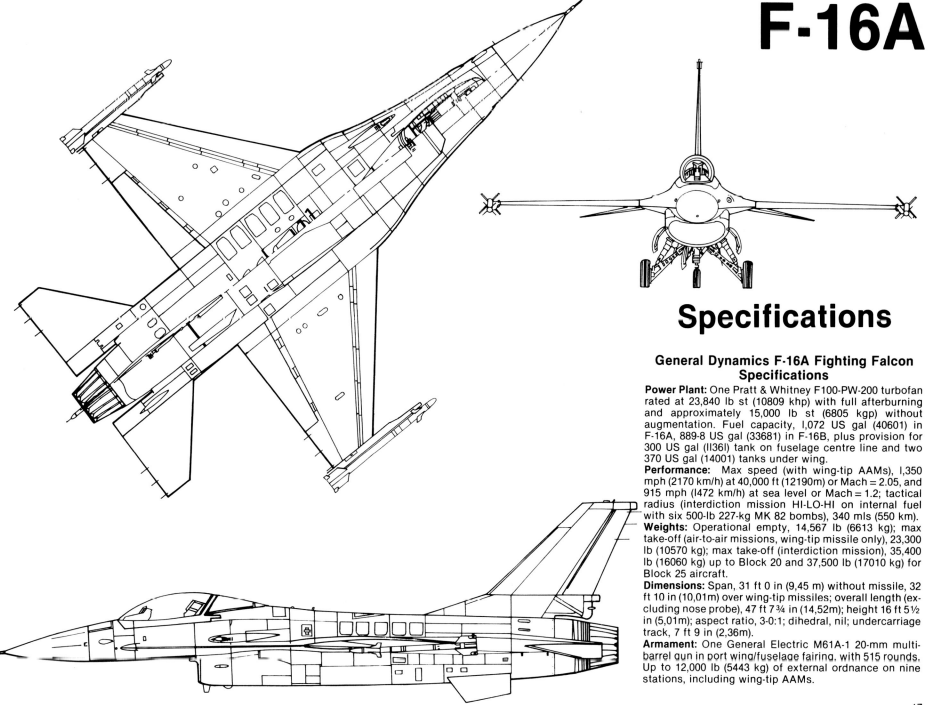

F-16A

Specifications

General Dynamics F-16A Fighting Falcon Specifications

Power Plant: One Pratt & Whitney F100-PW-200 turbofan rated at 23,840 lb st (10809 khp) with full afterburning and approximately 15,000 lb st (6805 kgp) without augmentation. Fuel capacity, I,072 US gal (40601) in F-16A, 889-8 US gal (33681) in F-16B, plus provision for 300 US gal (Il36l) tank on fuselage centre line and two 370 US gal (14001) tanks under wing.

Performance: Max speed (with wing-tip AAMs), I,350 mph (2170 km/h) at 40,000 ft (12190m) or Mach = 2.05, and 915 mph (l472 km/h) at sea level or Mach = 1.2; tactical radius (interdiction mission HI-LO-HI on internal fuel with six 500-lb 227-kg MK 82 bombs), 340 mls (550 km).

Weights: Operational empty, 14,567 lb (6613 kg); max take-off (air-to-air missions, wing-tip missile only), 23,300 lb (10570 kg); max take-off (interdiction mission), 35,400 lb (16060 kg) up to Block 20 and 37,500 lb (17010 kg) for Block 25 aircraft.

Dimensions: Span, 31 ft 0 in (9,45 m) without missile, 32 ft 10 in (10,01m) over wing-tip missiles; overall length (excluding nose probe), 47 ft 7¾ in (14,52m); height 16 ft 5½ in (5,01m); aspect ratio, 3-0:1; dihedral, nil; undercarriage track, 7 ft 9 in (2,36m).

Armament: One General Electric M61A-1 20-mm multi-barrel gun in port wing/fuselage fairing, with 515 rounds. Up to 12,000 lb (5443 kg) of external ordnance on nine stations, including wing-tip AAMs.

(Above) Belgian Test Pilot Serge Martin checked out in the YF-16 in December, 1978. (General Dynamics)

(Above left) Israeli Air Force Chief Test Pilot, Lt. Col. I. "Jeff" Peer completed several evaluation flights in the YF-16 prototype in July, 1979. The Number two prototype was used, and the Israeli flag replaced the Iranian flag on the forward fuselage for these tests. (General Dynamics)

Gun Drive Bulge

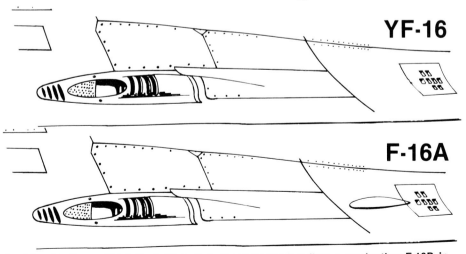

YF-16

F-16A

Austrian Air Force Chief Test Pilot, Col. Josef Bernecker flew a production F-16B in September, 1980 during the Austrian evaluation of the F-16. (General Dynamics)

The first production aircraft in the paint shop. (General Dynamics)

FSD aircraft with 370 gallon wing tanks and practice bomb dispensers on left wing station.

F-16A
Speed Brakes

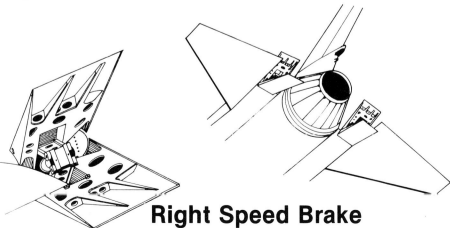

Right Speed Brake

As a result of the signing of the Camp David Accords, Egypt became a valued ally of the United States. The Carter Administration offered F-16s to Egypt at the beginning of 1980, under a plan called Project Peace Vector. (U.S. Army M-60 tanks were also included in the deal.) The only possible snag was money. As a client of the Soviet Union, Egypt had not had to pay for it's weapons. After it kicked the Russians out, but before it signed Camp David, the Saudis had offered to finance the westernization of Egypt's armed forces. Camp David isolated Egypt from the rest of the Arab world, and for the first time, the Egyptians were faced with financing their own weapons purchases.

President Sadat of Egypt offered the use of the Egyptian bases, which served to smooth the way to favorable terms, and the Egyptians signed a letter of agreement to procure 40 F-16s, along with weapons, spare engines, and a simulator. The $961.1 million deal was signed in June.

The following month the first four Israeli airplanes to be delivered to Israel (The Israeli's had been training in their own airplanes at Hill AFB) were flown from Pease AFB, N.H. to Israel in an 11 hour, 6,000 mile ferry flight, supported by multiple aerial refuelings. July 1980 was also the month in which the Air Force officially christened the F-16 the 'Fighting Falcon'. (A grass roots movement to name it the 'Condor' received little, if any, official support.)

But, by that September, when the F-16 made it's first appearance at the Farnborough Air Show, the Consortium was voicing concern that they would have to shut down their production lines if additional third country orders were not forthcoming within the next few months. (The Dutch were the only members of the Consortium to agree to purchase additional F-16s, having made the decision to replace their NF-5s.)

The first flight of the F-16/79 took place in October, followed in November by official certification of the F-16 as combat ready in USAF service. The 300th production F-16 was

Simple geometry of the fixed-ramp inlet to the F-100 engine. (GD)

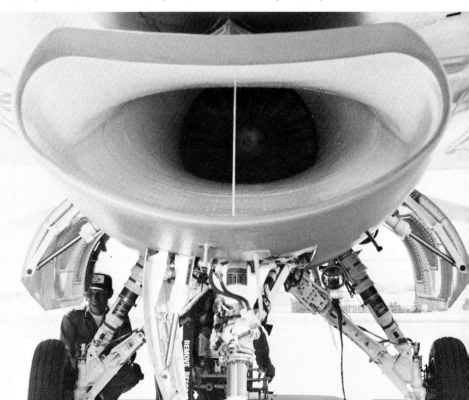

delivered in December, 1980, to USAF, and another development version of the F-16, the F-16/101, made it's first flight. In January, 1981, the F-16/79 completed it's development flight test program, and the Belgian Air Force's 349 Squadron became the first F-16 squadron to qualify for NATO service in Europe. In February the F-16 was refueled from a KC-10 for the first time, and launched the first Advanced Medium Range Air-to-Air Missile (AMRAAM), which was expected to become operational by 1985, after a competitive fly-off between Hughes and Raytheon had determined who would produce the new missile.

The Presidential Elections of 1980 had swept out the Carter Administration, and it's confusing and ineffectual foreign policy. The new Administration was expected to look more favorably upon military sales to friendly foreign governments, regardless of what liberal American interpretation of their 'human rights' policies was. General Dynamics was actively trying to sell the F-16/79 to Austria and Taiwan, and in April, 1981, they hosted Korean Minister of Defense Choo Young Bock in Fort Worth, impressing him with the F-16's capability with an orientation flight. This visit had been arranged as a result of the Reagan Administration's decision to sell South Korea 36 F-16As.

The F-16 was proving itself economical as well as effective in it's operational assignments. During Coronet Falcon, the 4th TFS deployed from Hill AFB, Utah to Flesland Air Station, Bergen, Norway, with a 10 hour, non-stop flight. The F-16s did this with three refuellings, the last a precautionary move in case bad weather was encountered at the destination. Lt. Col. Gary Michels, C.O. of the 4th, and a veteran of a similar F-4 deployment, stated that the F-4 would require 7 or 8 refuellings for the same mission, and would have used more than five times as much fuel. The F-16s encountered extremely harsh weather during this deployment, but still maintained a high rate of sorties, with a high degree of weapons delivery accuracy.

That deployment was followed by an even more impressive demonstration of the F-16's operational capabilities. In June, 1981, a team of F-16s participated in the RAF bombing competition at Losslemouth, Scotland. They won the competition handily, scoring a total of 7,831 points out of a possible 8,000. The Second place team was 1,430 points behind. Competition was supplied by RAF Jaguars, and Buccaneers, and by USAFE F-111s. In the bombing sorties, the 7 F-16s from the 388th TFW demonstrated the precision accuracy of the weapons delivery system by delivering all ordance on their assigned targets, airfields and convoys, in realistic wartime scenarios. The F-16s were the only aircraft in the competition to hit *all* targets in two days of bombing runs against a convoy of moving vehicles.

In addition to bombing accuracy, the competition put a premium on survivability, low-level navigation, and aircraft maintenance effectiveness. Four sorties per day were flown by the five competing teams, with points awarded for survivability and accuracy.

The air-to-air threat was provided by RAF Lightnings and Phantoms, which attempted to intercept from within five minutes of takeoff, until the F-16s had landed. The F-16s not only were *the most accurate* bombers, they also scored *86 kills in air-to-air combat, with no losses!* By contrast, the four other teams suffered 42 losses to the air-to-air threat, while scoring only one kill in defense. Ground crews averaged a 10.5 minute turn-around in refuelling and rearming with six MK-82 500 pound bombs and 515 rounds of 20MM ammunition.

That same month the F-16 received it's baptism of fire, dropping bombs in anger for the first time. The Israelis, unwilling to allow an avowed enemy to begin manufacturing the stuff of possible nuclear holocaust for Israel, launched a premptive strike on the Iraqi nuclear reactor at Baghdad. Eight F-16s, loaded with a pair of 2,000 lb. bombs each, flew the 600 miles from Etzion AB in the Sinai to Baghdad without the benefit of aerial refueling. They were accompanied by 6 F-15s flying CAP. The Israeli strike force used Jordanian frequencies and call signs, and spoke Arabic over the radio as they crossed northern Saudi Arabia pretending to be Jordanian Air Force pilots on a training mission. The ruse worked perfectly and the Israelis destroyed the Osirak Nuclear Reactor without being challenged by the Iraqi Air Force. In a gesture of disapproval for the Israeli action, President Reagan temporarily suspended shipment of further F-16s to Israel. This in an effort to uphold Ambassador Philip Habib's attempts at an accomodation with the Syrians, who had moved SAMs into Lebanon in an effort to forestall further Israeli raids on PLO camps in Lebanon. The Syrian SAMs could have become the spark which ignited another mideast

war, and the Reagan Administration was eager to have them removed. After the initial furor over the raid on Iraq died down, shipment of the remaining 22 of the 75 F-16s ordered by Israel was resumed. The Syrian SAMs stayed in Lebanon.

In July the Austrians decided against buying either the F-16 or F-16/79. Their reasoning was based upon Austrain nuetrality, which is mandated by their constitution. They felt that buying aircraft from one of the possible protagonists in any east-west war would weaken that neutrality, as perceived by the other side. Instead, they opted for the Mirage 50, but not until the French had reworked their prices to get them below those of both

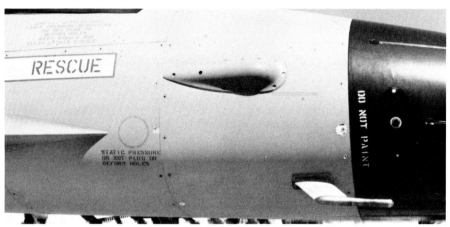

Nose detail showing one of two threat warning antenna (bulge) and the TACAN antenna. (under nose) Probe is for air data computor. (Dave Mason)

Strakes were applied to the top of the fuselage of the number one FSD aircraft during the test program, probably to ensure deployment of the spin chute. (Dave Mason)

models of the F-16.

Earlier in the year the Pakistanis had ordered 40 F-16s, which were scheduled for delivery in 1985. That was apparently an unacceptably long lead time for the Pakistanis, and they requested that at least some F-16s be delivered sooner. Accordingly, USAF asked Belgium and Holland to divert 7 to 9 aircraft from their production. Holland agreed immediately to turn over 2 or 3 aircraft to USAF, for transfer to Pakistan. They indicated that their production was at least that far ahead of schedule and therefore their air force would not suffer. Belgium took the request under advisement. This sale was followed by the announcement that 24 F-16s would be sold to Venezuela, with deliveries beginning in 1984.

The first F-16s to be based overseas were assigned to the 8th TFW 'Wolfpack' at Kunsan Air Base, Korea in September. The second overseas unit to re-equip with the F-16 was the 50th TFW at Hahn Air Base, Germany. They began turning in their F-4s that fall, and the first operational F-16s arrived in December. The first Egyptian F-16 was accepted by Major General Mohamed A. Hamid Helmi, EAF Chief of Staff, during ceremonies at Fort Worth on January 15, 1982. The first Egyptian F-16 Regiment was formed at An Shas, a fighter base northeast of Cairo. The Egyptian F-16s were painted in the standard USAF grey camouflage to ensure distinction from the Israeli F-16s.

In March it was announced that F-16s would be supplied to the Air National Guard and the Air Reserve. The first guard unit to receive the F-16 would be the South Carolina Air National Guard's 169th TFG, which would have 24 F-16s at McEntire ANG Base near Columbia, beginning in 1983. The F-16s would replace A-7s. The first reserve unit to receive the F-16 would be the 466th TFS, which would turn in it's F-105s. The 466th is based at Hill AFB, Utah. It was also announced that Shaw AFB, South Carolina would become the next F-16 base, with operations beginning in July, 1982.

Even an aircraft as sophisticated and technologically innovative as the F-16 is subject to growth. The rule of the 1980s seems to be increasingly dynamic operational situations, and in order to survive and succeed in this environment, the combat aircraft of the 80s and 90s will have to be adaptable. The F-16 is uniquely adaptable because of it's design and the USAF, realizing this, authorized General Dynamics to institute a program of redesign, where necessary, to take advantage of new avionics and weapons systems. This program got underway in 1980. It is known as Multinational Staged Improvement Program (MSIP), and will have three stages.

Stage one of MSIP will be incorporated in all aircraft in blocks 15 and 20, which will include the 456 F-16s scheduled for production from November, 1981 through November, 1984. In Stage I additional wiring will be added to facilitate introduction of new systems at a later date, some structural strengthening will be undertaken in the equipment bays behind the cockpit and to allow the carrying of an additional 1,000 pounds on wing stations 3 and 7. All of the above are internal. The only noticeable external changes are the addition of the fairing under the rudder fitted to all Norwegian F-16s for a drag chute, and to Belgian F-16s for the Loral Rapport III ECM, and an enlarged horizontal tail, whose rear outboard corners have been clipped to provide ground clearance.

Stage II will be incorporated in 1984, and will include addition of the improved Westinghouse APG-66 radar, a new Marconi HUD to be used with the Martin Marietta low altitude navigation targeting for infra-red (LANTIRN) that will be introduced in MSIP stage three. Stage III aircraft will have their gross weight increased to 37,500 pounds. The weapons and fire control computers in MSIP Stage two aircraft will have an avionics package that features an increase in computational ability to five times that of it's predecessor. The computer will have a 600,000 programmable memory, and will be capable of processing more than 500,000 operations per second.

Other capabilities planned for Stage three aircraft include the General Electric 30mm GEPOD gun, Maverick Missiles and Seek Talk secure voice communications system. The AMRAAM is planned for introduction in 1985, and will give the F-16 BVR capability. Improved ECM capability will be provided by a new jamming system under development by Westinghouse/ITT and Northrop/Sanders. At this time, it is planned to include MSIP Stage one in all export F-16s. Stages two and three may be included, depending upon political and/or security considerations at the time of their introduction.

SIIS Ejection Seat

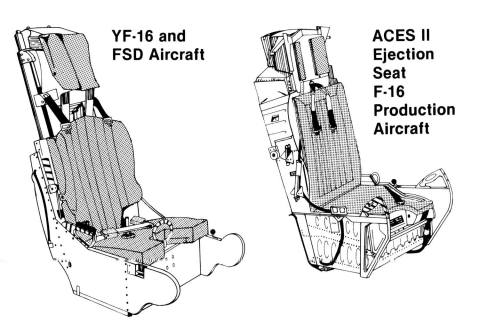

YF-16 and FSD Aircraft

ACES II Ejection Seat F-16 Production Aircraft

Late production model F-16A, with enlarged horizontal tail surfaces and added threat warning antenna at base of rudder. (General Dynamics)

21

Nose gear. Large black "bump" under intake is a threat warning antenna, while blade antenna is for UHF/IFF communications.

Nose Wheel

Nose Wheel & One Piece Door

Main Landing Gear

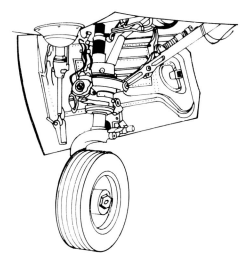

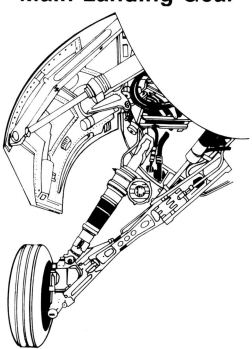

Extended tail hook. (Author)

Ground crew interrogating the F-16's Built In Test Equipment (BITE) to determine the presence of any discrepancies. (SSGT Roy Chismar)

(Below) Comparative sizes of the F-4 and F-16 are eivdent in this shot of a test flight about to depart Edwards. Veteran pilots compared the technological jump from the Phantom to the F-16 as being similar to that experienced when transitioning from propeller aircraft to jets in the 1950s. The F-16's turn radius is half that of the F-4 at similar altitude and Mach number (SSGT Roy Chismar)

Auxiliary power unit used to start the F-16. (Author)

Behind the Nose Cone

AN/APG-66
Fire Control Radar

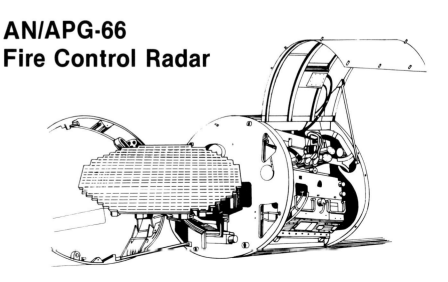

THE F-16B

When the first two seat version of the F-16 was proposed, it was with a lengthened fuselage. This would have required significant changes in the basic design and was eventually changed in favor of the current layout. The F-16B retains the same dimensions as the F-16A, with the exception of range. (The B model loses 1,200 pounds of internal fuel capacity because of the second seat.) The USAF announced plans to acquire 204 F-16s and the NATO consortium planned to add 98 to their air forces. The first two F-16Bs were the full scale development aircraft used by the Joint Test Team to validate design parameters. These aircraft have been used in a variety of test programs since. One was modified to test the feasibility of producing a Wild Weasel version of the F-16B. For these tests, antenna pods were fitted on the wingtips in place of the AIM-9 missiles normally carried, and compatibility of the F-16's pylon carriage system to such weapons as the AGM-45 Shrike, AGM-78 Standard ARM, AGM-88 HARM, and AGM-65 Mavericks. The second F-16B FSD aircraft has been leased back to General Dynamics and modified into the F-16/79 prototype.

F-16A

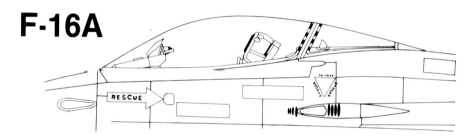

F-16B

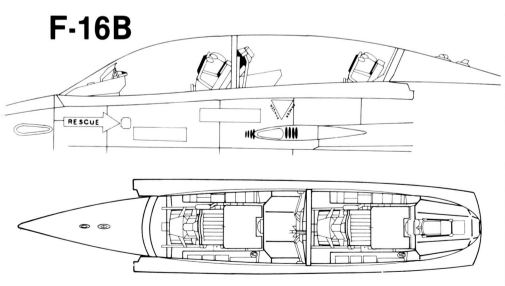

The primary difference between the F-16A and B is in the cockpit area, the B model having the second seat. (General Dynamics)

The first of two F-16B FSD aircraft was rolled out and flown on August 8, 1977 by Neil Anderson and Phil Oestricher. It made two flight that day, and on the second went to 30,000 feet and Mach 1.2, maneuvered through a 6G turn, and demonstrated no appreciable differences in performance with the A model. (General Dynamics)

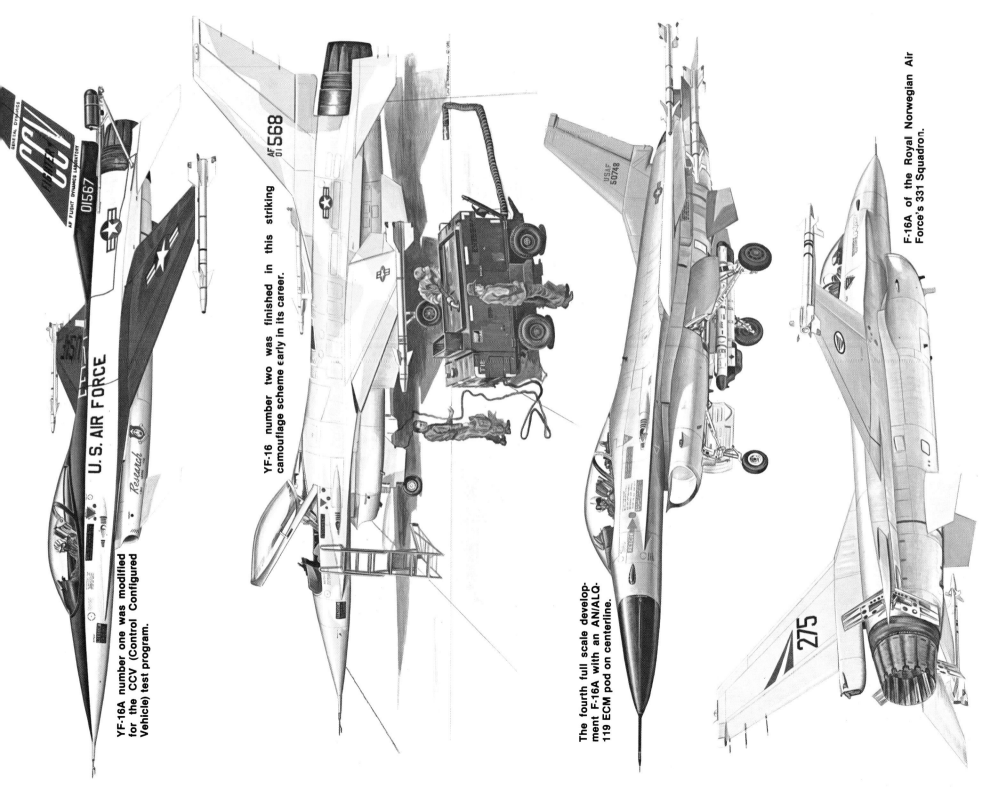

YF-16A number one was modified for the CCV (Control Configured Vehicle) test program.

YF-16 number two was finished in this striking camouflage scheme early in its career.

The fourth full scale development F-16A with an AN/ALQ-119 ECM pod on centerline.

F-16A of the Royal Norwegian Air Force's 331 Squadron.

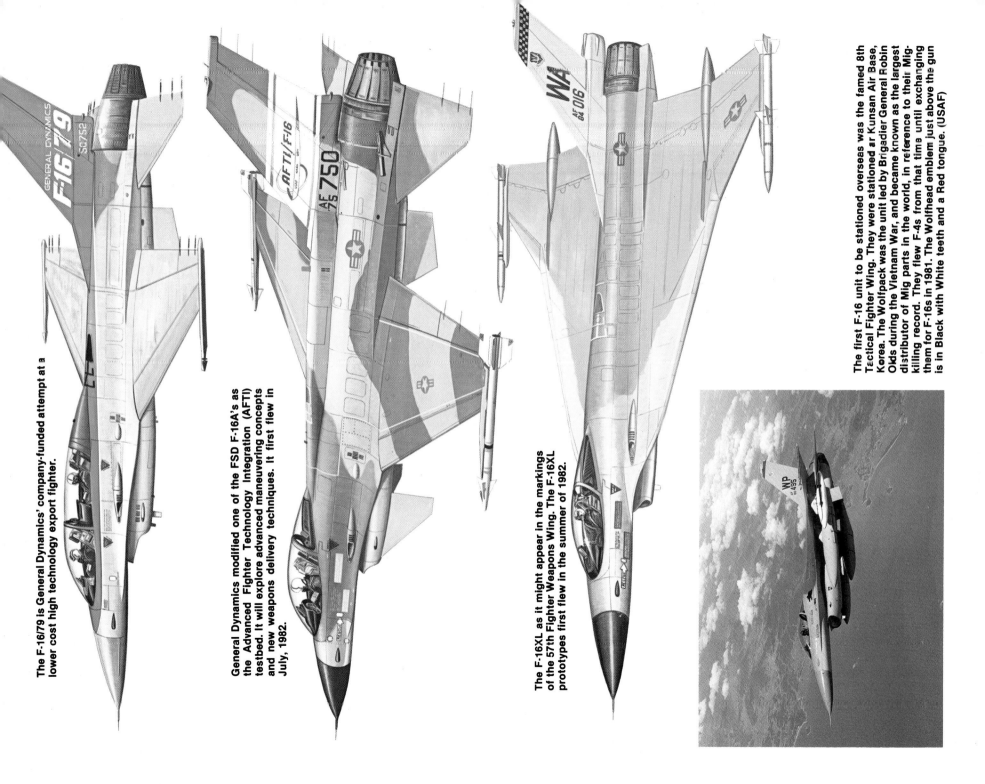

The F-16/79 is General Dynamics' company-funded attempt at a lower cost high technology export fighter.

General Dynamics modified one of the FSD F-16A's as the Advanced Fighter Technology Integration (AFTI) testbed. It will explore advanced maneuvering concepts and new weapons delivery techniques. It first flew in July, 1982.

The F-16XL as it might appear in the markings of the 57th Fighter Weapons Wing. The F-16XL prototypes first flew in the summer of 1982.

The first F-16 unit to be stationed overseas was the famed 8th Tactical Fighter Wing. They were stationed ar Kunsan Air Base, Korea. The Wolfpack was the unit led by Brigadier General Robin Olds during the Vietnam War, and became known as the largest distributor of Mig parts in the world, in reference to their Mig-killing record. They flew F-4s from that time until exchanging them for F-16s in 1981. The Wolfhead emblem just above the gun is in Black with White teeth and a Red tongue. (USAF)

(Above) F-16B-5-CF of the 324th Test Wing, Eglin AFB, Florida as it appeared in March, 1981. This is a production aircraft, used by AFSC to test weapons delivery and develop techniques. (Norman E. Taylor)

(Below) Visibility from the large clamshell canopy is impeded only by a single frame member. (Author)

(Below) F-16B of the 388th TFW thoroughly opened up for a phase check at Hill AFB. (SSGT Roy Chismar)

(Above left) The first FSD F-16B just after liftoff with the two General Dynamics test pilots aboard. Because the 25,000 lb. thrust F-100 turbofan engine provicdes a thrust to weight ratio roughly on the order of 1.4 to 1, acceleration is rapid and must be checked to ensure that the 300 knot landing gear transition limit is not exceeded. (General Dynamics)

The second FSD F-16B was evaluated by Group Captain Brick Bradford of the RAAF. A total of ten RAAF pilots flew the F-16 during an evaluation program that included 21 flights in 1980. In spite of this they selected the F/A-18 as their next tactical fighter. (General Dynamics)

F-16 pilot completes a preflight. F-16's ability to pull 9Gs on a regular basis makes the G suit the most important item in the F-16 pilot's wardrobe. (SSGT Roy Chismar)

F-16B-1-CF of the 16th TFTS, 388th TFW, September 1981. (H. Scharringa via Norman E. Taylor)

THE F-16/101

The number one Full Scale Development F-16A was fitted with a version of the General Electric F-101 engine in 1980, for a 100 hour flight test program. The F-101 engine had been developed for the B-1 bomber, and was the subject of a joint USAF/Navy project to develop an alternative engine for the F-16 and F-14. The Navy has lobbied hard for a more powerful engine for the F-14, and during the time it was thought that the Navy would *have* to accept a version of the F-16 as it's lightweight fighter, efforts to develop a common engine made sense. During the joint development program, the F-101 was known as the F-101X. It uses a core engine from the F-101, with a scaled-up fan and augmentor nozzle from the F-404 engine, and in it's final version has been known as the F-101DFE. (Derivative Fighter Engine.) Ironically, the F-404 is the engine used in the lightweight fighter that the Navy eventually selected, the F/A-18 Hornet. The first flight of the F-16/101 took place on December 19, 1980. The significant external difference between the F-101 powered version and the F-100 powered production F-16 is in the exhaust nozzle of the engine. The F101 engine is in the 29,000 pound thrust class. Upon completion of the F-16 flight test program, the F-101 engines were turned over to the Navy for flight testing in the F-14.

THE F-16XL

As good as the F-16A is, there is an even better version currently under development at General Dynamics, the company-funded project was known as Supersonic Cruise Aircraft Modification Program (SCAMP). It was later changed to the F-16XL, still later to the F-16E, and of this writing it is once more designated F-16XL. The F-16XL will employ a cranked arrow delta wing, which will increase wing area of the standard F-16 115%. The 70 degree/50 degree leading edge wing sweep is anticipated to reduce supersonic wave drag by 17% and reduce low speed pitch-up tendencies. The larger wing area will also allow an increase in fuel capacity of almost 4,000 pounds in the wings, and the two fuselage plugs added to accomodate the larger wing (overall fuselage length is 56 inches greater) will allow an increase in internal fuel of 1,800 pounds. All of this will add up to 45% greater range, with twice the payload of the F-16A, or 124% greater range with the same payload as the F-16A. The F-16XL will take off and land in two thirds of the distance required for the F-16A. It will have sea level penetration speeds 90 knots higher than the F-16A, and all that wing area will allow external loads to be hung in tandem, missiles to be mounted semi-submerged, which will reduce drag. The 9G maneuver envelope will be doubled, which will double or triple the gun firing chances in air-to-air combat. Perhaps best of all, these quantum leaps in capability will come relatively cheaply. The F-16XL will share 87% of it's basic structure with the F-16A, and will fly with the F-100 engine, though it could become a candidate for the F-101DFE or the Pratt & Whitney PW-1130 of 30,000 pounds thrust. General Dynamics has leased two of the FSD F-16s back from the USAF, and they will fly as F-16XL/A and F-16XL/B in 1982. The two seater will compete with the F-15 Strike Eagle as the all-weather fighter of the future, and with it's tremendous range and low level speed, it should be a prime candidate to replace the reconnaissance Phantoms in the USAF inventory.

F-16/101   F-16A

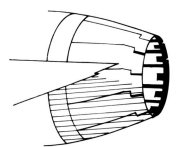
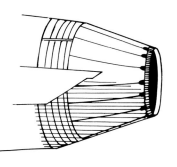

F-16XL Scamp

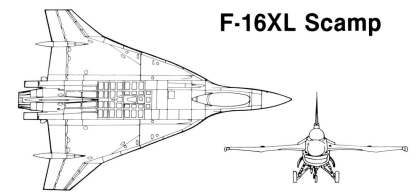

"FLYING THE F-16"

During my research for the F-16 in Action, I was fortunate to be able to interview General Dynamics' Director of Flight Test, Phil Oestricher, who participated in the testing of the prototypes and the initial production aircraft. The first flight of the F-16 was an unexpectedly memorable experience for Phil:

It was January 20, 1974, and I was conducting a high speed taxi test at Fort Worth, just to test the steering and brakes, making sure that everything worked as advertised for the official roll-out ceremony, since we taxied the airplane to the reviewing stand under it's own power. After that, the airplane was disassembled, and flown to Edwards AFB aboard a C-5, where it was reassembled and we began the flight test program.

It was a Sunday afternoon, and naturally, there was not much going on at Edwards. We were able to accomplish the 35 and 80 knot tests, verifying steering and brakes fairly quickly. I taxied back to the departure end of the runway and waited for the brakes to cool, and the wind to subside to an acceptable level before going for the 135 knot test. The profile for this test actually included lifting off and flying about a foot or so above the runway for maybe a thousand feet, then easing off the power, touching down, and braking to a stop. This would verify brake and steering actions, and give us some idea of how the airplane would handle in flight. It was the last step before the official first flight.

Things went awry though. The airplane got into a lateral pilot-induced oscillation, and it was a very rapid one at that...something on the order of 10 roll cycles in 14 seconds. At that point, I had little choice of actions, since the airplane was beginning to drift to the left side of the runway. I powered it up and just sort of let go and the airplane just flew off the runway very smoothly once I quit irritating it. I stayed in the landing pattern and came around and made a relatively uneventful landing. We hadn't intended to fly in a noticeable way that day, but we did. Incidentally, I was impressed with the way the marketing/public relations people got around our UNOFFICIAL first flight. They just called it 'flight zero', and that made the next one number one!

The problem on that first flight was in the flight control computer. We had programmed roll command gains of about twice what we should have had. Despite all the simulator work we had done, the roll command gains were too high. Even after this experience, when we rechecked the simulator it still didn't look as though we should have had a problem. But before we made the OFFICIAL first flight, we installed a manual control over the roll command gains. Takeoff and landing commands were done about half those in effect during flight. Production aircraft have this done automatically according to the position of the landing gear handle.

On the first official flight, we didn't attempt anything spectacular, preferring instead to limit the flight envelope to modest numbers while we did the basic systems checks and airspeed calibration.

I wondered if there were any additional surprises, after the incident with the flight control system on flight zero. According to Phil, all of the additional surprises were pleasant.

I had just finished checking out in the Phantom, and become used to the roaring and bellowing of it's Environmental Control System (ECS). The ECS in the F-16 was dead quiet...not a whisper! And then, I nearly ran everyone else in flight out of gas. By the time we landed, I still had about 45 minutes left, while they were running on fumes. That was our first real experience with the great range of the airplane.

When I asked how stable the F-16 is, Phil had this to say:

Well, I would say that it is perfectly stable. Of course, the way that the flight control system works, you have the sensation of flying part-

ially in an autopilot mode. For instance, if you trim the airplane for level one G flight, the system will maintain that. You might put it in a ten degree banked turn, let go, write something on you knee pad, then look up and find the airplane right where you left it. It just doesn't have the tendency of other airplanes to wander around the sky if you let go of the controls. You would never know, from flying the airplane, unless you were told, that it is statically unstable in pitch. The control system totally masks that feature. The airplane is actually trying to diverge all the time, but the sensors in the flight control system constantly correct this tendency. If the horizontal tail were to lock in the neutral position, the airplane would wildly diverge...either pitch up or pitch down depending mostly upon which direction the nose was moving when it locked. The F-16 is the only operational airplane that flies statically unstable. If you fly formation on the 16, you will see the horizontal stabilizer dithering up and down, maybe a quarter of an inch, constantly correcting this latent instability. Now, all this was done for a reason. We did not want the horizontal stabilizer to be fighting the wing when we were turning. In an airplane like the Phantom, for instance, the tail is creating a substantial down load in order to trim the airplane to the higher angle of attack the wing needs to create the lift .In the F-16, we will kick the horizontal stab leading edge to start the turn...that gets the pitch rate going. Once the commanded G is established, the tail returns to neutral. Now, the wing, the tail, and the fuselage are lifting surfaces. The whole airplane has become a lifting surface, which is why it turns so well on a relatively modest wing area, and why it accelerates so well in the turn.

We appear to have the only airplane that was optimized for maximum aerodynamic efficiency at some elevated angle of attack. This is a result of the blended wing/forebody design. In straight and level cruise flight, we actually pay a small penalty in drag from the vortex generated by the fuselage strakes. But pull it into a turn, and the F-16 really comes alive! Every other airplane I can think of is optimized essentially for the cruise condition.

That, of course is not the only unusual thing about the F-16. One of the most talked about features is the seat...or rather, the way that the seat is installed in the airplane. It is tilted back at an angle of thirty degrees, which puts the pilot's heels at about the same level as his posterior. Phil's comments on that are enlightening.

The tilt-back seat is just the greatest thing going! The G's are very easy to take...just the other day I was pulling 9 G's, and didn't even start to grey out! The reason for that, of course, is the way that you sit in the airplane. The heel rest line is so high that your buttocks are

A pair of F-16s from the 388th TFW, the first operational unit to get the F-16. The closest machine carries a centerline tank. (USAF)

The first production F-16A was delivered to Hill AFB in January, 1979 and began operations with the 388th FTW's 16th TFTS (Dave Mason)

actually the lowest point of your body, and since you are tilted back, the vertical distance from your heart to your brain is also less. In all other airplanes, when you pull G's, the blood tends to pool in your lower extremeties, and the first thing that happens is that you lose vision. In the F-16, the blood flows from your legs **down** to your posterior, which creates pressure for the blood to return to the heart...it's a kind of natural G suit effect. I have been able to prove this to myself by making a direct apples to apples comparison between the F-16 and the F-4. On the same day, with the same G-suit and regulator, I have flown both airplanes. I gained a solid one and a half G's in the F-16 for the same physiological sensations. I have been able to fly a steady 6 G's for a minute and a half, and seven for a minute. The only funny thing that happened was that I lost control of my breathing. I never had any grey out...could function perfectly normally...I just couldn't talk...I found myself inhaling in the middle of a word. Apparently, my diaphragm got messed up by the constant G load. The other great thing about the seat position is the fact that your weight is distributed over a greater area when you are pulling G's, which makes for less discomfort. Then too, when you are pulling very high G's, you are in a hard turn and probably looking out the top of the canopy. With your head back against the headrest, you are already looking in the right direction, which makes for fewer knotted neck muscles after a flight. Makes a lot easier to look behind you too...all you have to do is rotate your head, while it is against the headrest.

One of the most commonly heard complaints about the multi-mission F-16 is that it is not as effective an air-to-air machine because of the compromises made to equip it for air-to-ground missions. I asked Phil if the performance had been noticeably degraded with the addition of the air-to-ground capability.

Not particularly. After all, if you are not actually carrying the bombs or the racks, the capability is only represented by some software. That is, the cards that allow you to project tracking or bombing solutions onto the HUD (Head-Up Display). Aerodynamically the airplane is the same, and there is not enough weight in the software to make any difference, that I could see, in the airplane's performance. Strictly speaking, I suppose you could say that there is some penalty for the enhanced wing structure that allows us to carry bombs, but it is really very little.

Phil's experience as a Marine fighter pilot included time in the FJ Fury series, the Cougar and Panther, the F4D Skyray, and the Crusader. He had amassed over 5,500 hours in fighters by the time he started flying the F-16. I wondered what, besides the very obvious technological pioneering, was the most impressive thing about the F-16, in his mind.

I have been flying this class of airplane now for twenty seven years, so it is hard for me to project myself into the boots of a guy right out of Undergraduate Pilot Training — to understand how he views this new fighter...the first that he will fly. But doing that, I guess I would have to say that the most impressive thing about the F-16 is that it is a tremendous confidence-builder.

It is a very honest-handling airplane. It's really difficult to get into trouble with the F-16 by mis-handling the controls. Like any airplane, you can fly it out of control if you really try. You can go straight up until you stop, and slide back, at which time you are technically out of control. Of course, shortly thereafter, you'll be back in control...the airplane we are producing now, if flown at any reasonable CG, in that situation will just flop around a little, point it's nose at the ground, and fly away.

The most dreaded situation in an air combat mission, aside from getting waxed by the

bogie, is the stall/spin. For years, young fighter pilots have lived in fear of departing their airplanes and ending up in a flat spin, which it was probably not possible to recover from. I wondered how the F-16, with it's marvelous fly-by-wire computerized flight control system handled this age-old problem.

That is part of the confidence-building package. All of the airplanes we have built, from the original small tail YF's, to the current larger horizontal-tailed versions, have what we call a yaw rate limiter. If, somehow, you have managed to thwart the basic angle of attack and structural limiting scheme, and you have gotten the airplane out of control, ...let's say that your angle of attack exceeds 29 degrees...if there is any yaw present, the system will sense it and put in opposite rudder, and pro-aileron. The system assumes that the airplane is spinning. We departed the airplane many times during the high angle of attack program and had it come out by itself. By the way, the pilot is locked out of the system at this point...he can put in all the control commands that he wants and the airplane will ignore them. It's just as though you had an electronic instructor pilot riding with you, who would take the airplane away from you when you got into trouble, then give it back once he had the situation under control.

Does that mean that if I pull the airplane up into a stall, then stomp full rudder when the stall breaks, that it won't spin? (The traditional method of getting an airplane into a spin.)

Well, you really can't even stall the airplane. A nice demonstration of this is Mach 1.2 at 30,000 feet, roll into a 90 degree bank, and haul the stick all the way back, and hold it. The airplane responds with a very nice turn. Then pull the throttle to idle. The airplane continues to decelerate, and as it does, you can play the turn, rolling out wings level at 105 knots, 25 degrees angle of attack...the airplane continues to fly! The flight control system is not allowing the airplane to be flown out of control, so long as you are flying on the wings. Now, if you go ballistic, as in going straight up until the airplane stops, then your aerodynamic controls can't work and you can fool the system. It also has G limiting. In the air-to-air configuration, no matter how hard you pull back, it won't go over 9 G's. We have a switch in the airplane, which we select for either air-to-air or air-to-ground missions. In the air-to-ground mode, you are limited to 16 degrees angle of attack. You can still pull 9 G's, but the flight control system will not allow you to manuever beyond the limits set for a particular mission. The whole idea behind this limiting scheme is to allow the pilot to put all of his attention on his adversary...on hitting the target, without having to sit there and monitor his own airplane. I can recall going up to do ACM in a Crusader, and spending half my time watching angle of attack and airspeed to make sure that I didn't end up in some godawful falling leaf or spin. In the F-16, you just totally ignore everything else and concentrate on the other guy. That's the "unloader" for the new pilot, and it should build confidence rapidly. Here he has an airplane that is not going to jump up and bite him.

Actually, we have less trouble with the new guys than with some of the older heads, who might have a thousand or more hours in some thing like the F-4. We tell them they don't need the rudder pedals. Once airborne, you can put your feet right back against the seat, if you want to. In fact, I have advocated that the rudder signal be disconnected with the gear handle up. In normal flying, there is no reason whatsoever to use the rudder. The airplane coordinates it's turns. It likes to roll on aileron, it does not like to roll on rudder. If you get the Phantom into a high angle of attack, low airspeed situation, you had better roll on the rudder, or you will depart the airplane. The F-16 rolls very nicely on aileron at high angles of attack. During the test program, we were able to depart the airplane by using a lot of rudder at high angles of attack. As a result of these tests, we have now programmed the system to take away rudder as the angle of attack increases, so that at max AOA, you do not have pilot commanded rudder available.

The F-16 begins to emerge as the ideal airplane...incapable of abberational behaviour...able to turn inside of almost anything...with a flight control system that protects it's pilots, even from themselves. Why then, are F-16's crashing?

*Several of us on the program thought the accident rate might be high. This airplane gives you a King Kong complex – that you are almost invincible. I predicted that the accidents would be due to low pull-outs...a guy staying on the bombing run too long because he knows the F-16 will get him out in a hurry...he eats up the clearances and flies into the ground, or into another airplane if he is engaged in ACM. Even experienced pilots have to be careful that they don't paint themselves into a corner that even the F-16 can't get them out of...all because the airplane makes you feel as if there is nothing you can't do. As one Navy pilot, who evaluated the airplane, said; "If I'm here, and I want to be there, I just sort of THINK there, and I **am** there! Furthermore, if I want to get from here to there, I just plug in burner and point the airplane and I'm there. I don't have to think about accelerating to pick up speed and wait for optimum speed before turning...I just point it, and I'm gone.!"*

One of the most unique configurations applied to the YF-16 was the Control Configured Vehicle. A pair of canards were added just behind the intake, and with these additional control surfaces, the YF-16 was able to perform manuevers that defied aerodynamic law, as practiced by conventional airframes. I asked Phil to describe his experiences with this version of the F-16.

I only flew it once, since I was not prime on the program, but that one flight was very, very interesting. There are ever so many modes in the thing. You can implement fuselage pointing. For example, you can point the nose up, down, or sideways, while maintaining the same path vertically, and horizontally, through the sky. It is most interesting in the lateral mode, since it would allow you to make a strafing pass on a vehicle that was crossing in front of you, maintaining the proper lead on him, without using aileron to coordinate your nose pointing. It gives you instant correction of your error. You can do dead level turns in the airplane, which are very uncomfortable, since you are sort of plastered against the outside of the turn, against the cockpit wall.

It also has the capability to translate vertically without changing the pitch attitude of the airplane. That was done by operating the flaperons in conjunction with the horizontal tail. The canards – which by the way, seems like a poor term – I always think of them as forward rudders were used in conjunction with the lateral manuevers. For instance, let's say you put in rudder. Now you put in counteracting force with the forward rudders. The rudder would create yaw in one direction, while the forward rudders were counteracting the yaw. The result would be a lateral displacement, without yaw.

We limited ourselves to a little less than one G laterally in the CCV airplane, because our accelerometers went off scale at one G. But the airplane came very close to having the capability to fly a sustained one G laterally. Now that, with the right kind of fuel and oil system, would have given you the capability to create the most spectacular air show in history! Consider the possibilities; You could have come along, rolled into a 90 degree bank, and flown your whole show in that attitude. Or, you could roll one way, while turning in the opposite direction. When you consider that people are conditioned to expect a left turn when you roll left, then to see you go in another direction...well, it would be tough to comprehend as a spectator.

There was one other mode in the CCV airplane, which though not as spectacular as some of those we have mentioned, was probably the most useful to a fighter pilot. It was called manuever enhancement. In the standard airplane, when you want to initiate a climb, you pull the stick back, the trailing edge of the horizontal tail goes up to establish the pitch rate. That decreases lift momentarily, and the airplane actually has a tendency to drop before increased angle of attack takes over and the airplane starts up. With manuever enhancement, when the trailing edge of the horizontal tail went up, the flaperons were displaced downward symetrically, and the net result was an upward force from the first instant of control displacement. It gave a crisper response, and also provided better gust response. One of the great mysteries of the program, to me, is why manuever enhancement didn't end up being a standard feature in production airplanes.

At this point in our conversation, we were joined by Neil R. Anderson, General Dynamics Director of International Flight Evaluation and Engineering. Neil was one of the initial YF, F-16 test pilots, and did much of the air show flying at Paris and Farnborough.

My experience in other high performance airplanes had pretty well convinced me that there was some portion of the performance envelope that would yield airframe buffet that was at the very least uncomfortable for the crew. I asked them where that point occured with the F-16.

Neil: *You can pretty well say there is none. For instance, we start to get buffet that you would call buffet in a turn at something above 6 Gs. Neither of us has ever flown an airplane in our lives that would go that high buffet-free.*

Is there any difference between sub-sonic and supersonic flight?

Phil: *Only at about .9 Mach. There is a little area there in which the aerodynamics are just unstable enough that even perfect leading edge flap positioning is not going to stop all separation* (of the airflow over the control surfaces) *That is pretty common among all airplanes. If it is going to tremble, then it will do it at .9 Mach.*

Neil: *That's as much a shock wave consideration as it is an airplane buffeting consideration. It's kind of hard to tell the difference between shock buffet and any other kind of basic airframe buffet.*

Phil: *In any case, with the F-16 there is no wing rock, and any slight amount of buffet there might be is meaningless in terms of aircraft control.*

F-16A of the 57th Fighter Weapons Wing, Nellis AFB, Nevada Detachment 16 of the 57th FWW was responsible for testing and data collection which led to establishment of operational guidelines for air-to-air and air-to-ground missions. The Multinational Operational Test and Evaluation team (MOT&E) was formed by th 57th. It consisted of personnel from TAC, ATC, AFLC, AFSC, and AFTEC, as well as representatives of the NATO consortium. Eighteen pilots (10 American and two each from the four NATO countries) conducted a year of intensive testing, including deployments to each of the NATO countries that were buying the F-16. Nearly 5,000 missions were flown in over a year of testing, the results then tabulated and condensed into reports for each of the air forces participating. (K. Minert via Norman E. Taylor)

F-16B of the 474th TFW, Nellis AFB, Nevada. The 474th became the first operational wing of F-16s without a training or other function associated with introduction of the F-16 when they turned in their F-4 Phantoms for Fighting Falcons in November, 1980. (Author)

Neil: *That is probably best illustrated when you consider that you can fly the airplane at 95 knots, for instance. You just slow the airplane down, and as you do, whether the flaps are up or down, the leading edge flaps are programmed to extend. Now, that program is based upon angle of attack, of course, but the effect of it is to eliminate buffet...that's what it's all about. After the leading edge flaps are all the way out, then you might start to feel some very light buffet. At 95 knots it is so light that it is really inconsequential. As a matter of fact, you might want a little more than the airplane gives you, just as a reminder that something is going on out there that the pilot should be watching a little more closely.*

Phil: *We have a standard check that we make on all the production airplanes, which we call the low speed warning tone, and I guess most pilots would think of this as a stall-warning horn. We establish a 50 degree climb with reduced power settings. The warning tone is programmed to come on at 111 knots, plus or minus 31 knots. At that point I can initiate a full aileron 180 degree roll and pull the stick full aft...the airplane responds crisply, and I think the lowest speed I have seen in doing the manuever is 90 knots. Just try that in a Phantom and see what happens!*

Neil: *In a Phantom, or any F-14, or an F-104, or an F-111...anything else you want to try it in, you're in for a very unpleasant experience!*

As you might well imagine, by this time I was beginning to think that there was nothing the F-16 wouldn't do, and do with enough grace and civility to make the peerage green with envy. Was there anything it wouldn't do? I asked them to tell me something bad about the F-16.

Neil: *Oh, we can tell you several bad things about the airplane. There's not enough thrust to weight. It's got more than any thing else, and there's still not enough. It's got more visibility than anything else, and there is still not enough. The pilot sits higher than in any other airplane we have ever flown...he's still not high enough.*

Phil: *The landing gear is too close together. Of course, there was no place else to put it, but we would still like to have it as far apart as on a 106.*

But aren't these criticisms generated by the very characteristics that make the F-16 better than most of it's contemporaries?

Neil: *Yes sir. But neither one of us will ever say that this is the epitome of what a fighter should be. It's not. The seat is inclined at 30 degrees, which makes it much better than other fighter seats. That only tells us that tilting the seat was the right way to go. Maybe a future fighter should have the seat tilted at 45 or 60 degrees. (The USAF Aerospace Medical Research Laboratory did conduct tests of a 65 degree tilted seat, using a 19 foot closed-loop centrifuge to subject test subjects to a constant 7 Gs while they performed target acquisition, tracking, and firing solution tasks.)*

Phil: *If I am pulling a lot of G, I am going to be going there (pointing up), so there is really no reason to be looking over the nose. Therefore, it is much more comfortable to be reclined in the seat, with my head against the headrest.*

Neil: *When you are pulling 7 Gs, and your 25 pound head weighs 175 pounds, it is much easier to keep it against the headrest, rotating it in place as necessary to look to the side or behind you. It is also much easier on you, physically, to have your weight distributed over your entire back while pulling those Gs, rather than concentrated where you sit. The fighter pilots who fly our airplane for the first time notice those kinds of things...those are the features which they appreciate the most. We have also provided a great deal of rudder pedal travel for forward and aft adjustment. In fact, there is much more there than would be needed just to adjust from the smallest to the tallest F-16 pilot. The reason for that is that on long ferry flights, you are actually able to crank the rudders all the way forward and literally stand up, scratch your back, and stretch. Believe me, that makes a big difference on those long deployments.*

It is also apparent that the F-16 has much more than it's share of pioneering technological innovation. Where did all these great ideas come from? They certainly were not just happy accidents, were they?

Phil: *Well, as far as the seat is concerned, the Crew Station Design Group (they still use the old bomber terminology fostered by Convair's great bomber building tradition) had some ideas on seat tilt. They had a mock-up which could be tilted to various positions, and we thought 30 degrees felt pretty good. In the prototype airplanes, we had the capability to remove a couple of pins and return the seat to a more normal orientation of 17 degrees, but the thirty degree position was so good that that was never done. We had a very strong input on canopy design. Naturally, the aerodynamicists wanted a very small canopy to reduce drag. But we maintained that 'if you can't see out of it, it's not a fighter' and our reasoning prevailed. Then the idea to put the canopy on the right way, instead of backwards, as everyone has been doing for forty years, was put forward. I mean, you don't need mirrors in this airplane...you can turn you head and see behind you...so you don't need a canopy frame to hang mirrors on. The canopy itself is ¾ Polycarbonite, which makes it the strongest canopy in the world, bar none. It is amazingly flexible though, and we have set up ground test bird strikes that created dents in the canopy the size of half a football. The dent would become a crease and the shock traveled rearward over the canopy, and it was possible that the pilot might get knocked on the helmet as it passed over his head. This, of course, happens in the fraction of a second, then the canopy rebounds to it's normal shape. Now, if you hit a bird going fast enough, it will come through the canopy, but this canopy is capable of taking much more punishment than any other. And the latching system is so effective that we were able to remove some of the redundancy designed into the prototypes, and we have never had a canopy loss on any F-16. Those pilots who have ejected from the F-16 have not reported anything unusual in that operation either.*

Well, who shepherded all these great ideas through the design team? How much of the design was computer-generated?

Phil: *Harry Hillaker is the man I consider most responsible for the design of the F-16. Harry is one of those gifted preliminary designers who has probably not gotten anywhere near the acclaim that he deserves. Everything that he has worked on has turned out super, and that includes such airplanes as the B-58. What he did with the F-16 was to lay out reasonable approaches to the problems we were trying to solve, then let the wind tunnel dictate which were worth pursuing. We had a tremendous amount of wind tunnel time with the F-16 design before the prototype ever flew. It was much, much more than you would have expected from a minor 38 million dollar research program. Of course, we hoped that it would lead to more than just a research program.*

It has turned out to be much more than a *modest research program*, and may just become the most popular jet fighter in the free world.

FLYING IN THE F-16

The United States Air Force inventory, past and present, is filled with aircraft whose "official" nicknames have been colloquially altered to fit the perceptions of the troops who have flown and maintained them. These are the names you will hear in the briefing room, on the flightline, or in the bar, but never, never in any official press releases. After all, what self-respecting General would want it known that he commanded a wing of Hogs? Or Lead Sleds? Or Thuds? or Goonies? Or Warthogs? Or Big Ugly Fellows? (Which, incidentally, did not begat the Short Little Ugly Fellows.) The list goes on and on, and includes some marginally acceptable names like Hun, Deuce, Six, or SPaD. (These names didn't make the official releases either.)

The official names look great on paper. For instance, what could be more warlike than "Thunderbolt"? It fairly reeks of aerial destruction. But, to the troops who flew and maintained it, the P-47 performed like a juggernaut, looked like a jug, and became "Jug" forevermore.

Could anything carry more cargo than a "Skytrain"? But, does anyone remember that the venerable C-47, which certainly carried more than it's share of cargo, was given that official name? Nope, they remember it as the "Gooney Bird". The same process of metamorphosis occured with a score of others, some to become legendary, (Skyraider to SPaD) others losing their mantle of immortality (Hercules to Herky). No matter how good the name looked on paper, if the troops weren't comfortable with it, it got changed.

The USAF has christened it's newest jet fighter "Fighting Falcon". The Falcon is the bird other birds fear. It is a relentless predator, and can be trained to a fine edge of aggressiveness by it's master. It is the mascot of the United States Air Force Academy. "Fighting Falcon" is a name with a lot going for it, and should be popular with everyone in the Air Force, right? Wrong! The popular lexicographers in the Air Force didn't know a whole hell of a lot about the Fighting Falcon, but they did know that the F-16 was very different from it's predecessors in one fundamental way. It is the very first fly-by-wire airplane in the inventory. Ergo...******THE ELECTRIC JET!******

That is an unpretentious name, yet one that excites the imagination. Though "Electric Jet" is certainly in reference to the circuitry of the F-16's flight controls, it is a name that conjures up visions of something more. Perhaps the crackling excitement of some long forgotten heroic novel...(TOM SWIFT...and...HIS ELECTRIC JET!) Or maybe the awe-inspiring sight of the F-16 cranked into a 6 G turn, vortex-generated contrails streaming over it's wings as it effortlessly maintains this manuever. But it is probably most appropriate in describing that first flight in the F-16 which, for me, was an *electrifying* experience.

Before I could fly in the F-16, I had to renew my AF Form 1274. That meant a day of physiological training, and a flight in the altitude chamber at MacDill AFB. The Aerospace Physiological Training Unit, USAF Regional Hospital, MacDill AFB, Florida, is responsible for the administration of the physiological training programs at MacDill and Tyndall Air Force Bases. It is the only unit of it's type within the Air Force with a foreign language version of it's curriculum, and has provided training for most of the air forces of Central and South America. The boss of this diverse and very professional outfit is Lt. Col. Allan L. Fox who did most of the lecturing during my day and a half of instruction. (Since I was receiving "Passenger" training, I was only required to complete the first half of the three day course.) This was not my first experience with the altitude chamber and attendant physiological training, but it was by far the most interesting and informative session I have spent on this subject. Al Fox has a style of teaching that keeps the entire class involved, and interested.

The cover of the aerospace physiological training booklet issued to us contained this quotation; "Aviation in itself is not inherently dangerous, but like the sea, it is terribly unforgiving of any carelessness, incapacity, or neglect." One of the advantages enjoyed by military aviators over most of their civil counterparts is their preparation for operating in the ocean of air that surrounds the earth. That preparation includes an extensive knowledge of the characteristics of the atmosphere and how it affects the respiratory and circulatory systems of the human body. For seven hours of that first day we were indoctrinated with the hazards of high altitude flight. The balance of the day was spent in a briefing on oxygen equipment in current USAF use. I can't honestly say that all of this put my mind at ease concerning the upcoming chamber flight to 35,000 feet. But knowing how to recognize the symptoms of hypoxia, hyperventilation, and the various decompression sicknesses, and what to do about them, coupled with the fact that we would be accompaned on the flight by members of the physiological training unit did spread a veneer of fatalistic acceptance of the upcoming ordeal.

The danger involved in the high altitude flight, assuming that you have an adequate oxygen supply, is in the decrease in atmospheric pressure. The higher you go, the more danger and/or discomfort you are liable to. At 63,000 feet you cross Armstrong's Line, and without pressurization or a pressure suit, you will not recross that line alive, oxygen or no. Rapid ascent to high altitude in an unpressurized vehicle can cause evolved gas sicknesses such as the bends, and to prevent that we spent thirty minutes breathing 100% oxygen before beginning our chamber flight. This cleansed our circulatory systems of nitrogen, which would come out of solution and form bubbles at altitude.

There were 15 students on that chamber flight, and two volunteers had agreed to remove their oxygen masks at 35,000 and 30,000 feet, respectively, to demonstrate to the rest of us the effects of hypoxia. (Oxygen deprivation.) At 35,000 feet the normal person will last about a minute without oxygen. That is, he will be able to function in a rational and effective manner for about a minute. Of course, individual tolerances will vary, and our first volunteer made it to a minute and a half before hypoxic symptoms rendered him incapable of going back on oxygen without repeated and insistant urging from one of the instructors. Our second volunteer removed her mask and shut off her oxygen at 30,000 feet. She confounded the normal tolerance curve by going a good four and a half minutes before going back on oxygen. At 25,000 feet all of us removed our masks, in two shifts.

The principle danger of hypoxia is that it's onset is insidious. Under controlled conditions such as the altitude chamber, it's symptoms seem easy enough to detect. Unfortunately, it is most likely to occur when you don't expect it, and the stress of flying your airplane may serve to both accelerate and mask hypoxic symptoms. Each of us was given a clipboard containing an Hypoxia Worksheet. This was filled with such common questions as; "What is your spouse's name? How many vowels are in the name Christopher Columbus? How many three cent stamps are in a dozen? What are your symptoms of hypoxia at this time?" There were also several math problems. If you were able to com-

The author gets the word on what does what from Tom Dean before their flight in the F-16B.

plete this sheet without any symptoms, you were instructed to count backwards from 100 by threes. It was a very effective means of demonstrating the incapcitating effects of hypoxia. I became lightheaded, then dizzy. A tingling sensation seemed to crawl across my skin, which was being subjected to hot and cold flashes. I couldn't seem to concentrate on the paper, but that was O.K. The euphoric indifference of terminal hypoxia had begun to set in when an alarm went off in my head, urging me to hit those switches on my oxygen regulator which would give me 100% oxygen under positive pressure. The good news about hypoxia is that recovery is rapid and complete with the application of oxygen.

As we descended, we were required to clear our eustacian tubes to prevent the pressure differential between outside and inside the ears from causing damage to the ear drums. (The ears automatically adjust during ascent.) The accepted method of ear-clearing is via the Valsalvo maneuver, in which your mouth is closed, your nose is held closed, and you blow against this pressure. We were advised to Valsalvo every 1,000 feet on the descent, but not more often that that.

At 18,000 feet we paused and removed our masks again. We were given multi-colored cards, with letters printed in the segments of the color-wheel configured charts. The lights were turned down, and we received graphic evidence of the effects of moderate-oxygen starvation on night vision. Though there were several shades of color on the wheel, and several letters superimposed upon them, the colors appeared gray and the letters were difficult and sometimes impossible to pick out. When the oxygen was turned on, the colors leapt off the card and the letters came into focus.

There was one more event to experience before my altitude chamber flight could be considered complete, and that was an explosive decompression. Anyone who has flown on an airliner has received the standard airline briefing on decompression, designed to give you the information you need to survive without unduly alarming you. That is the bare minimum. On the other hand, Hollywood has made the explosive decompression much more of an event that it really is. You certainly will not be sucked the length of the airplane through the hole that caused the decompression. Nor will you experience immediate strangulation. In our decompression, the section of the chamber we were in was at 6,000 feet, while the adjacent section was at 30,000 feet. The airlock was opened with a loud bang, and the pressure differential that resulted from trapped air caused our masks to momentarily be lifted from our faces. A fog formed as our altitude stabilized at 22,000 feet, but quickly dissipated. And that was it...we descended, and I stepped out to receive my fresh chamber card. Now I was ready for the real thing.

The 61st Tactical Fighter Training Squadron is one of four squadrons within the 56th TTW, which is the operational training unit for pilots transitioning to the F-16. The 61st is commanded by Lt. Col. Milan Zimer, a veteran of 220 combat missions, with three Mig kills to his credit. He is what you would expect a veteran squadron leader to be...tough but fair, popular but respected. He has the outgoing personality of the prototypical fighter pilot that disarms you immediately and makes you feel as though you have known him for years. He is totally sold on the F-16, and is convinced that had he been flying the F-16 in Southeast Asia, he would have been a triple ace. His combat experience has given him a perspective on the F-16 that is becoming increasingly unique in the Air Force today, as more and more combat veterans retire from the active force. That combat experience came up continually in our discussions of the F-16's capabilities, as he compared what he had done with what he would have been able to do with the F-16 . I was anxious to fly the mission on his wing.

I would be riding in the rear seat of an F-16B. My pilot was Captain Tom Dean, one of the hard-charging young officers who came into the Air Force in the wake of the Vietnam War. Tom had worked his way through college as a flight instructor and already had 1300 hours, and a flight instructor's rating when he joined the Air Force. In the course of his 10 years in the Air Force, he has accumulated 1075 hours in the F-4, and 680 hours in the OV-10. His 2 ½ years in the OV-10 were the toughest of his career, as the inbred fighter pilot in him revolted at the droning around at modest speed. His assignment to the F-16 has made all of that worthwhile as he, like all F-16 pilots that I talked to feel they are flying the epitome of fighter aircraft.

Briefing for the flight was at 0730. We were scheduled for an 0940 takeoff. The mission was air-to-ground, with a low-level route to the range at Avon Park. We would be carrying three BDU-33 practice bombs on a Triple Ejector Rack (TER) and six Mk-106 practice bombs in an SUU-20/A practice bomb dispenser. We also had 120 rounds of ammunition loaded for the M-61 Vulcan cannon. During the briefing, I was given the mission overview, and told what to expect, and what to look for in the Radar Electro Optical (REO) display. The REO dominates the instrument panel in the rear cockpit and consists of a large cathode ray tube on which you can select the radar picture which the pilot is currently painting, or the view through the Heads Up Display (HUD). Zimer and Dean went over the mission carefully, using video tapes of previous similar missions to illustrate what we would be doing and what I could expect to see in the REO. The briefing lasted until 0900, at which time Tom and I picked up our route books and headed for the personal equipment shop where we got into G-suits and torso harnesses. (He slipped into his with practiced ease, while I attempted to maintain a studied nonchalance as I struggled into mine.) Then it was out to the airplane for the preflight before climbing aboard.

The weather in central Florida during May is liable to be anything from hot and humid to monsoon, with all the variations in between. As we walked to the airplane, the skies to the west were relatively clear, while off to the east, in the direction of the range, there was a lot of low, broken clouds. This mission required a ceiling of at least 4,500 feet, with 3 miles visibility. Since the cloud deck was forecast to be scattered to broken, and the visibility requirements were more than met, we weren't worried about getting the mission in. (They weren't worried...if they didn't fly today, they would fly tommorrow. Me, I was damn worried. This might be my only ride in the Electric Jet, and I wanted to get the most out of it.)

Getting into the rear cockpit of the F-16B requires either a short agile pilot, or a damn careful tall pilot. Since I am closer to the latter, some experimentation was necessary before I finally folded it all into place. The problem is the canopy rail, which forces you to bend nearly double before gingerly sticking your foot into the tunnel which houses the rudder pedal. No doubt practice makes this easy, but the Air Force seems disinclined to accept this as a valid reason for additional rides in the F-16, so I did the best I could. Once you are in the seat, with the G-suit hose, survival kit straps, lap belt, and parachute risers snapped into place, you can appreciate the comfort of the 30 degree tilted seat. That is, until you realize that you still haven't attached your cru 60 fitting to your torso harness, and plugged in the oxygen mask and radio lead. But that proved to be surprisingly easy too and there was little to do until Tom climbed aboard and cranked it up.

Unfortunately, Colonel Zimer's airplane had developed an hydraulic leak and could not fly. It was a chance to demonstrate another of the F-16's strong points. With no spare aircraft in our configuration, he ordered the entire ordnance load offloaded and put on another airplane. About the time that I was becoming uncomfortably hot under the mid-morning sun, and Tom was thinking about having me climb down, Zimer's crew was completing a 35 minute download-upload on his bombs and bullets. He flashed Tom a thumbs-up, and they climbed into their cockpits to fire up the 25,000 pound thrust P&W F-100 engines. With the engine running and the canopy down, the air conditioning began to make the cockpit downright pleasant. Tom went through the checklist quickly, and the crew chief waved us out of the parking spot. Before we had taxied, Tom loaded our route waypoints into the inertial navigation computer, which will use great circle steering

Col. Milan Zimer, Commanding Officer of the 61st TFTS, flying wing

signals, displayed as steering commands on the HUD or REO to direct the pilot to and from the target. The pilot never has to look in the cockpit for the correct navigation information, but should he need backup confirmation of what he sees on the HUD, it will also be displayed on the Horizontal Situation Indicator (HSI) and on the REO. Up to 10 waypoints can be stored and retrieved by rotating the destination thumbwheel on the Fire Control Navigation Panel (FCNP). In the Nav mode the HUD will show a flight path marker which represents the aircraft, and a steering bar to right or left of the aircraft. In order to follow steering to a selected waypoint, the pilot need only hold the flight path marker on the steering bar, though Colonel Zimer emphasized that during training the pilots were urged to maintain their own VFR and dead-reckoning navigation as a back-up to the system. The HUD also shows G-loading, Calibrated airspeed, Mach number, magnetic heading, nautical miles to destination, time to destination, altitude, and maximum G the aircraft has pulled during this flight. In addition to that, it will tell you which of the 10 destinations you are heading for, confirm that you have the computer in Nav mode and show an air-to-ground target designator box. And that is only one of several modes available on the HUD, each with it's own set of special symbology, peculiar to the mission, whether it is air-to-air, air-to-ground, or just getting home on minimum fuel.

Tom also demonstrated the Stores Control Panel (SCP) and how it is managed. The SCP is just to the left of the HUD and contains an alphanumeric display in 5 horizontal rows of 10 characters each. All letters and numbers zero through nine can be displayed. Once the ordnance load is stored on this panel, the pilot no longer has to keep a mental inventory of what he has left, and where he has it stored on the airplane. The SCP will do that for him, displaying a continuously updated inventory. It will also provide automatic sequencing of all weapons and ideal release intervals and arming options for the type of target selected. There was plenty of time for all of this, since we were taxiing to runway 4, which is about as far from the parking ramp as you can get without sampling the waters of Tampa Bay.

We pulled into the last chance checkpoint, and the armament crews pulled safety pins from weapons pylons and the gun, while we kept our hands in sight. (No armament man wants to have his day ruined by an accidental release of a bomb while the safety pins are being pulled...once you leave the last chance area, you can do what you want, but while you are here, keep your hands off them triggers and pickle buttons!)

We lined up on the runway, in the lead position, with Zimer on our right wing. Tower cleared us for takeoff, and Tom smoothly advanced the throttle, while holding the brakes. Then as Zimer nodded that he had completed engine checks, he placed his head against the headrest, snapped it forward, and brakes were released in both cockpits. Now both throttles went to military power, and I got a taste of the F-100 engine's acceleration. It sent charges of excitement through me...the excitement you feel when experiencing raw power. I had my eyes glued to Zimer's airplane and saw his nose wheel lighten...just the extension of the nose gear oleo...that indicated his airplane was ready to fly, just a second sooner than ours. Probably, I reasoned, because we were carrying a centerline tank to make up for the lost fuel capacity that results from the addition of the second seat. Then we were off, gear coming up, turning right out of the traffic pattern, with Zimer flying a wing position that would be the envy of any Thunderbird.

Once we were established on course for our first turn point, Tom passed the lead to Zimer. Miami Center cleared us to 8,000 feet as we climbed between canyons of puffy cumulus. Later in the afternoon these clouds would build to impressive proportions and spawn some of the major league thunderstorms that are common to Central Florida in late spring. But for now, they made a beautiful backdrop as our sleek grey fighters climbed through them. Tom dropped astern of Zimer's F-16, and began to demonstrate the air-to-air mode of the APG-66 radar.

Like just about everything else in the F-16, the radar is almost pure Star Wars. A General Dynamics sales brochure description gives a good overview of it's capabilities and characteristics when it says; "The F-16's Westinghouse APG-66 fire control radar operates in X-band to minimize atmospheric degradation and uses low and medium-pulse Doppler techniques to allow clutter-free lookdown capability. The APG-66 radar is compatible with, and provisions have been made for, the AIM-7 missile." (Author's note: This would give the F-16 the much bally-hooed beyond-visual-range (BVR) capability that

defense critics have seized upon as a fatal flaw in the F-16's capability.) "Switches on the throttle, side-stick controller, or radar control panel allow the pilot to change radar modes quickly and with his head out of the cockpit — a significant advantage in critical air-to-air environments. These mode options include: *Search Volume,* which controls range, azimuth, and raster. *Missile Mode,* which provides fully dynamic launch parameters. *Air-to-Air Gunnery Modes,* which provide snapshoot no-lock-on, gunnery solutions based on bullet trajectory or utilizing a lead computing optical gunsight for fully locked-on gunnery solutions. The *Air Combat Mode,* which overrides all other modes, provides two different automatic lock-on modes. In the Air Combat Mode, the radar automatically searches and locks onto targets out to 10 nautical miles. After lock-on, full tracking parameters are displayed automatically on the HUD. All this is accomplished with one switch on the throttle."

Though they don't consider 10 miles beyond visual range, there are probably few, if any, fighter pilots that could spot a fighter the size of a Mig-21 at that range. The radar, in search mode will look in an area covering 120 degrees off the nose. In the dogfight mode, it will look at areas of 20X20 degrees or 10X40 degrees. When it locks onto a target, a target locater line will appear, running from the aircraft guncross, towards the target. The pilot turns the airplane along that line, and when the target is within the viewfinder range of the HUD, the tracking box on the HUD, will snap onto the enemy aircraft, whether it is within sight or not. When the firing parameters of the weapon selected are met, a flashing diamond on the HUD tells the pilot it is time to fire the missile, and splash one bandit. During the engagement, the HUD will show the Gs being pulled, the air speed, the Mach number, the gunnery mode selected in the computer, the altitude, a print-out of the fire control computer windows, and a pitch scale and horizon reference line. The wonders of this system, and it's reliability, were demonstrated to me as we made several S turns behind Zimer's airplane, at ranges of up to two miles, and angles-off of up to 45 degrees.

Miami Center cleared us into IR-46, the low-level training route we would be flying to the Avon Park Range. IR-46 starts at the Anclote Keys Special State Conservation Area, which lies two miles off the coast at Tarpon Springs. It follows the coast in a northeasterly direction to a point at the southern tip of the Chassahowitzka National Wildlife Refuge, 33 nautical miles from Anclote Keys. The run up the coast was spectacular. I don't believe there is a pilot alive who doesn't enjoy flying at low level, and at 500 feet above the blue green waters of the gulf, 450 knots of airspeed is impressive!

Dean and Drendel, post flight.

At point A, we turned inland on a heading of 075 degrees. Over the marshy green flatlands we maintained an altitude of approximately 1000 feet. Tom explained that in combat he would stay right down in the weeds, but the higher altitude we were flying was a safety margin and probably prevented the premature demise of an alligator or rattlesnake or two, not to mention the occasional fisherman we flashed over from time to time.

The clouds were thickening overhead, indicating a lot of convective activity in the atmosphere, yet the F-16 semed to be on tracks it was so rock-steady as we bored through the turbulent air. Tom had the radar in the ground-mapping mode, and by flipping the symbology control knob on the REO to radar, even I could pick out the distinctive outline of Lake Panasoffkee, which was just to the northwest of point B along our route.

As we flashed over the twin concrete ribbons of Interstate 75, Tom rolled into a hard turn to right, picking up a heading of 157 degrees for our run to Point C. Zimer now assumed the lead, and

I could see his airplane, spread in combat formation about a mile to our right. On this leg of IR-46 we were flying along a railroad track, and it showed up on the radar as a pencil line, with the junction boxes painting like widely space railroad ties. One of the dangers of low level flight is a chance of a bird strike. Though the canopy of the F-16 is the toughest of any jet fighter, a direct strike by one of the large birds that abound in Florida is going to shatter it. Suddenly there were flashes of white to left and right! We had split a flight of two birds. Zimer later said he believed they were Turkey Buzzards, easily large enough to do significant damage if you hit one.

As we ran southeastward at 450 knots, Miami Center called traffic. Most of it was well above our altitude, and the radar was able to lock several targets up, giving us the target's airspeed and heading. The relatively low speeds of these targets indicated that they were general aviation aircraft, which constitute a hazard too. Though the military low-level training routes are clearly marked on the Sectional Charts used by Private Pilots, there has been more than one case of a Cessna or Piper blundering through the restricted area of the ranges or following the railroad tracks that parallel IR-46. While the F-16 pilot is liable to be warned in advance by ATC or his own radar, the Private Pilot may never see the high speed jets. (Most GA aircraft are not renowned for the visibility provided from their cockpits.) There was not much in the way of scenery along this route, but it was still hard to keep my eyes on the radar picture on the REO. Now and then, an isolated sharecropper's dwelling would blur past, but for the most part, it was green desolation — still, at 450 knots, desolation is impressive just because it is going past so fast. Tom demonstrated the great acceleration of the F-16 by slowing down as we approached our turn point, then after turning to the new heading of 120 degrees, advancing the throttle. It gave us a noticeable boot in the back and we seemed to jump from 400 to 450 knots in milleseconds.

Now we were driving toward the Initial Point for our first bomb run. U.S. Highway 27 came and went, and a second later so did Haines City. Lake Hamilton and Lake Hatchineha appeared, then we were at the IP, just short of Lake Kissimmee, and Tom followed the steering bar command for a hard turn to a heading of 175 degrees for our run to the target. This was to be a radar lay-down of a simulated nuclear bomb, and he nudged the throttle forward to give us 460 knots of airspeed as we leveled at our bombing altitude of 1,000 feet.

The APG-66 radar is the star of this show too. In the air-to-ground mission, Visual, Electro-Optical, or Blind bombing options are available to the pilot. Our first delivery was via the blind bombing option, using the Continously Computed Release Point (CCRP) mode. The other option is Beacon Bombing, which is a combat-tested and proven method of computing a release point using signals from a transmitter with a known location, and offsetting the target. If I had been paying real close attention, I would have seen the symbology as the computer pickled off our bomb. I wasn't and I didn't, which was kind of a shame, since it only missed the center of the target by 37 meters, which is a whole lot closer than you have to get with a nuke. And one of the neat things about this mode is that after you pop up to get a good radar picture of the target, you can freeze it and you will no longer be radiating emmissions for the enemy to lock onto as you approach the target.

I have to confess that most of the bomb runs occured so fast that I did not get a real clear picture of what we were doing. I was too busy taking in the primary sensory perceptions to engage in much in the way of intellectual exercises. Though we were limited to 5.5 Gs with the SUU and TER on the wing stations, we still managed to keep our energy up, and to turn in incredibly tight circles as we followed Zimer in a left hand racetrack pattern around the targets. We made several passes at the range targets, which I remember as a kaliedoscope of gut-squeezing 5 G pull-ups, graceful pops to altitude, followed by precise rolling manuevers to line up the targets, and roaring down the chute. Survivability of the F-16 in combat should be good just because it does all of this in such a small area, and yet so fast...it is going to be damn hard for those enemy gunners to line up. And as accurate as it is, there won't be many second passes at targets.

I had looked forward to the strafe passes, just to experience the BBBBBRAAAPP!!! of that chain-saw M-61 cannon which would be firing next to my left shoulder, and to seeing the effects of the highly concentrated cannon shell fire hitting the paper targets set up on

The F-16B in which the author flew his low-level bombing mission.

the range. We had figured on two passes to use up the 120 rounds of 20MM ammunition. At the M-61's rate of fire, that would give us two ½ second bursts. Unfortunately, the ranger officer had cancelled all strafing because of the numerous puddles of water left by several days of afternoon thunderstorms. The danger of richochets was just too great to risk firing the guns. (Who needs to get shot down by his own gun?)

We pulled off the range, rejoined in echelon, and headed back in for an echelon attack, in which first the lead airplane, and then the wingman pulled (in this case, right) and popped up ten degrees to acquire the target before diving on it. Zimer had picked out a SAM site, and we were going after a 57MM AAA site. Once again, the fire control computer showed how the F-16 has become the most accurate dive bomber in the Air Force. Whereas, in previous jets, you had to have a precise dive angle, air speed, and mil setting in the sight, with the F-16 you need only put the bomb fall line in the HUD on the target, and the computer will do the rest with it's Continuously Computed Impact Point (CCIP) mode. This can be used to deliver conventional or laser-guided bombs, 2.75 rockets, or for gunnery with the M-61 cannon. There are only two things for the pilot to worry about: Wings level, and needle and ball centered with the bomb fall line on the target. When the pipper goes through the target, the bomb is pickled off. If the stick and rudder work is good, the bombs will be on target. We made one more circle of the range for my benefit, so that I could note the various targets, which include an airfield with several derelict aircraft (pretty thoroughly shot up), several trucks (same) and simulated SAM and AAA sites.

Then it was off the range and into the Lake Placid MOA, for my five minutes of glory. They had promised to let me fly the Electric Jet, and I was looking forward to it more than any combination of words in my Thesaurus can describe. I wasn't disappointed.

I slipped my right hand around the side stick. I was determined not to ham-fist the airplane. Let's see...I seem to remember a test pilot remarking that you only had to think "over there" and the airplane seemed to get there by itself. I applied a bit of pressure with my thumb, and it rolled into a right turn. Let go...it stayed there. This was where most experienced pilots who fly the F-16 for the first time go wrong. In a conventional airplane, when you roll into a turn, it is necessary to apply opposite aileron to stop the rolling motion of the aircraft. So, in a left turn, the natural control movements would be left stick until you had the desired angle of bank, then right stick to stop the bank and back pressure to hold altitude. If you try that in the F-16, you get what is called "roll ratcheting". Because the F-16 does exactly what you tell it to, the aileron you would normally put in just to stop and hold a bank angle will result in a roll in the opposite direction. A couple of turns, left and right, were all it took to get used to that. My first aileron roll was betrayed by extensive aerobatic time in the T-34. I pulled the nose up before starting. Tom must have anticipated this maneuver, because he stopped me before I had the nose five degrees above the horizon. Nose back down on the horizon, I rolled left, and as we reached the 270 degree position, I decided to lead the roll-out. Naturally, I ended up in a 45 degree left bank. You simply don't have to think about leading recovery of maneuvers that far ahead. The next few rolls, left and right, were much smoother, and recovery seemed to be right on wings level. I was really getting into this thing now! A few more turns, left and right, steeper bank, and a little pull...wow! This thing is really sensational! I have never experienced anything so responsive, so light on the controls, so positive in it's reactions to my control inputs, and yet so reassuringly comfortable to fly after just.. what?.. five minutes?

Unfortunately, Zimer had reached Bingo fuel state, and we had to rejoin and head back to MacDill. He contacted Miami Center for vectors, and we started down from the 14,000 foot altitude I had been playing with. As we bored into the weather, I suddenly realized that the sidestick was the natural position...having that thing waving around between your knees was damn inconvenient...and I hadn't noticed that the stick did not move. The amount of pressure exerted on the stick is what gives you your cues, not how far the stick moves. This airplane, with it's flight control computer, was really optimized for maximum pilot control, and the position of the stick and the thirty degree seat make it the most comfortable fighter ever. As we droned through the clag in close formation, Tom commented on what a good formation airplane it is..."And with a smooth flight lead, like Colonel Zimer, it's really easy." It sure looked easy, in spite of the fact that from our position within a few feet of Zimer's wingtip, there were several times when it became little more that a dark silhouette as we penetrated some of the darker clouds. Little wonder that the Thunderbirds have chosen the F-16 as their next airplane. Their audiences are in for some spectacular air shows.

We were handed off to MacDill Approach, and then to the GCA controller, who talked us down to within a hundred feet of the runway in formation. The formation was rock-steady throughout the entire approach and pull-up for a go-around. We came around the pattern once more in echelon, pitched out and, just as you would expect the perfect fighter to do, made a perfect landing. We had been in the air an hour and twenty minutes...the quickest hour and twenty minutes I have ever spent in an airplane...and the most...the most...well, like I said there aren't enough words in the Thesaurus. As we taxied back to hot-refuel the airplane so it would be ready for the next sortie, Tom asked me what I thought of the mission. I told him I thought they had better not give too many rides to Congressmen, because if they found out how much fun the airplane was, they would have some serious second thoughts about paying guys to fly it.

Since the stated goal of American Arms is to deter the other guy from starting a shooting war, the other guy's impression of our capabilities is important. Milan Zimer summed it up accurately and succinctly when he told me at the end of our interview; "If I were a Soviet, I think I would be extremely worried about flying against F-15s and F-16s. The two of them together are absolutely devastating!" If they're not worried about it, they should be...they'll be up against a whole generation of Luke Skywalkers!

The June,1982 Israeli attack of PLO positions in Lebanon graphically demonstrated the capabilities of the F-16/F-15 air to air combat team. While the F-15's flew high cover, the F-16's delivered their bombs with pin-point accuracy, and when challenged by Syrian Migs, the Israeli aircraft rolled up an absolutely astounding kill ratio. At this writing, Syrian losses have been quoted at anywhere from 60 to 80 Mig-21s and 23s, with no F-15s or 16s lost by Israel. Zimer's comment, made two weeks before these battles, had proven deadly prophetic.

The first Fighting Falcon for the 50th TFW takes off for it's European home at Hahn Air Base, Germany. The 50th was the second overseas wing to get the F-16. (General Dynamics)

A pair of F-16s over a castle on the Rhine. The 50th TFW is comprised of the 10th, 313th and 496th Tactical Fighter Squadrons. (General Dynamics)

F-16A-10-CF of the 19th Tactical Fighter Squadron, the first squadron within the 363rd TFW to equip with the F-16. The 19th was inactivated on 12 January, 1946 and had not been active since that time, until getting the F-16 in 1982. (Norman E. Taylor)

(Above) The first Dutch Fighting Falcon was this F-16B, assembled by Fokker-VFW in Holland. It made it's first flight in May, 1979. (General Dynamics)

(Below) The Dutch initially ordered 102 F-16s, but now plan to acquire an additional 111, and have placed an order for the first increment of 22, at a price considerably under the "not to exceed" price of $6.09 million 1975 dollars. (General Dynamics)

(Below) F-16A of the Royal Netherlands Air Force Number 322 Squadron at Leeuwarden, the first Dutch unit to equip with the Fighting Falcon. (Michel Klaver)

The RNLAF will replace it's NF-5s with F-16s and at least one squadron (Number 306) will equip with F-16s modified to use the Oldelft Orpeheus reconnaissance pods now used on it's F-104s. (Michel Klaver)

F-16A of 322 Squadron, RNLAF at Leeuwarden. Also based at Leeuwarden is Number 323 Squadron with F-16's and scheduled to equip with Fighting Falcons are Numbers 311, 312, and 306 Squadrons at Volkel. (Michel Klaver)

Multiple Usage of Parts

The horizontal tails, flaperons, and 80% of the main landing gear parts can be used on either side of the aircraft. A single integrated servoactutor is used in five places for control of the horizontal tails, flaperons, and rudder. Two actuator assemblies are used for the eight leading-edge-flap rotary actuators.

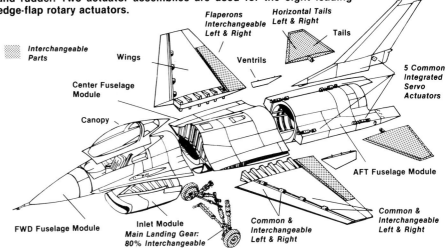

The first F-16 built on a European assembly line was this F-16B of the Force Aerienne Belge (Belgium), delivered January 26, 1979 at Charleroi-Gosselies airport. (General Dynamics)

(Below) This F-16B was loaned to General Dynamics, by Belgium, for the 1977 Paris Air Show. 349 Escadrille was the first Belgian squadron to operate the F-16, and the first European unit to be certified combat-ready by NATO (Michel Klaver)

(Below) F-16A of the Belgian Air Force at Wright Patterson AFB, July 1979. It was there for tests with Loral Rapport III internal ECM, which has passive and active modes. This unit will take the place of the standard USAF externally carried ECM pods (AN/ALQ-119 or AN/ALQ-131) and will be installed in Belgian F-16s beginning in 1983. It will be carried in the pod normally used to house a brake parachute, ala Norwegian F-16s. (Dave Menard via Norman E. Taylor)

41

Standard F-16A

Norwegian F-16 With Drag Chute

Norwegian F-16s are assembled on the Fokker-VFW line at Amsterdam. The first F-16 was delivered to Norway in January, 1980. The Kongelige Norske Luftforsvaret have ordered 72 F-16s, which are unique in having a fairing at the base of the rudder to house a drag chute, thought necessary because of the short runways and prevailing wet and/or icy conditions in Norway. The F-16 Operational Conversion Unit in Norway is Skv 332, at Rygge. The first operational unit was Skv 331 at Bodo, which traded their F-104s for Fighting Falcons. Skv 334 at Bodo, and Skv 338 at Orland are tasked for antishipping strikes, and will carry Bullpup missiles for that mission. (General Dynamics and Michel Klaver)

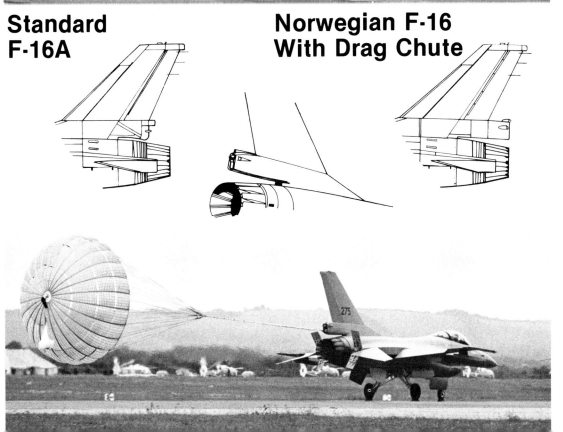

Denmark's initial order included 46 F-16As and 12 F-16Bs, to be delivered from the SABCA/SONACA plant in Belgium. The Kongelige Danske Flyvevabnet assigned the first of it's F-16s to Eskadrille 727 and 730 at Skrydstrup. They replaced F-100s. Danish NATO Missions include both air-to-air and anti-shipping strikes (General Dynamics)

F-16 Program Status

Air Force	Delivered In 1981	Delivered Through 1981	Total Contracted To Date	Current Acquisition Planning
United States	161	351	1,085	1,985
Belgium	20	50	116	134
Denmark	16	33	58	58
The Netherlands	22	51	142	213
Norway	18	30	72	72
Israel	39	75	75	150
Egypt	0	0	40	80
Pakistan	0	0	40	40
Korea	0	0	36	36
Venezuela	0	0	24	24
Totals	**276**	**590**	**1,688**	**2,792**

The first Fighting Falcon for the Israeli Air Force was turned over to Major General Arie Levy, Director of the Israeli Ministry of Defense Mission to the United States on January 31, 1980. It was flown to Hill AFB, where Israeli pilots joined the operational training program. (General Dynamics)

(Left) The first F-16s were delivered to Israel via an 11 hour, 6,000 mile ferry flight from Pease AFB to Israel. They carried U.S. insignia on their Israeli camouflage for this trip. (General Dynamics)

(Middle left) Israeli F-16A over Masada. (General Dynamics)

(Above) The first F-16A for the Egyptian Air Force demonstrates the Fighting Falcon's ability to climb straight up, accelerating. Because of the 30 degree reclined seat, the most comfortable angle for the pilot is the one demonstrated here. (General Dynamics)

(Left) The Egyptian Air Force accepted the first of its initial order of 40 F-16s in January, 1982. (General Dynamics)

F-16/79

As the first F-16As were entering operational service, General Dynamics began to look at the considerable market provided by those countries which would soon be thinking of replacing their F-5s. While the standard F-16 might be too expensive and/or more diverse than a particular air force might require, a less expensive alternative that retained the technological innovation of the F-16 should be a good product for this market...or so the corporate leaders at General Dynamics reasoned.

They were confident enough of this line of reasoning to propose a privately funded research project, combining the basic F-16 airframe with the time tested and proven J-79 turbojet engine. Market research had indicated the possibility of approximately 500 units, with development costs estimated at $20 million. ($12 million for the prototype airframe, and $8 million for three engines.) The version of the J-79 proposed for use was the -17X, which was estimated to have at least 90% commonality with the dash 17 and 19 engines used in so many export Phantoms and Starfighters, which provided yet another marketing advantage, since many of the potential customers for the F-16/79 would have experience with, and possibly retain some spares, for the J-79 engine.

Relatively few changes were required in order to fit the J-79 engine to the F-16. A longer aft fuselange fairing was required, and the air inlet had to be modified to fit the J-79's airflow requirement. The overall length of the fuselage of the J-79 powered F-16 was extended 2.54 feet. The number two F-16B full scale development aircraft was leased from USAF, and modified at Fort Worth. General Dynamics estimated that the per unit fly-away cost of the F-16/79 would be $1.2 million less than the F-16A. As the modification of the prototype continued, the General Dynamics international marketing team began researching it's potential in earnest. From a possible market of 500 aircraft they revised their estimates upward to over a thousand, with 20 different air forces identified as potential customers.

The F-16/79 made it's first flight on October 29, 1980, with company test pilot James A.McKinney at the controls. As the test program progressed, test pilots reported that the F-16/79 demonstrated the same 9G capability of the basic F-16. The area in which a major difference in capability existed was in acceleration, with the /79 requiring up to 30% more runway under similar conditions. Where it surpassed the F-100 engine's performance was in acceleration to top speed. The turbojet just seemed to perform more easily at or near Mach 2. As of this writing no F-16/79s have been sold, and the sole example of this version is the F-16/79B two place aircraft.

The F-16/79 taxies out for a demonstration of its ability to carry large ordnance loads, in this case, 18 500 lb. bombs. (General Dynamics)

F-16B

F-16B

F-16/79

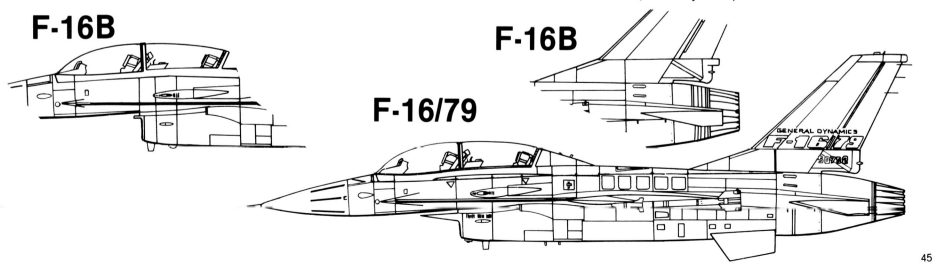

(Above and below) These photos show the primary difference between the standard F-16B and the F-16/79B. Below, the extended upper lip of the intake necessary to correctly position the supersonic shock wave for the J-79 engine is visible, while the picture above shows how far the exhaust has been extended to mc-comodate the J-79. The J-79-GE-17X used in the developmental program featured an enhanced thrust mode, which GE dubbed "Combat Plus", and claimed it would give the J-79 thrust nearly equal to the F-100 engine used in the standard F-16A. Unfortunately, like the water injection used in piston engines during combat emergencies, they severely limited its use. (1½ hours in the first 1,200 hours of engine operation.)

(Right) The F-16/79 prepares to refuel from a KC-135. It is loaded with AGM-65 Maverick misiles and 370 gallon fuel tanks underwing. (General Dynamics)

46

WEAPONS

The F-16 was designed as a simple, clear air mass, air-to-air fighter. As such, it was intended to carry only the basic rudiments (ala 1973) for air combat. At the time, this meant a gun and Sidewinder AAMs. The Fighting Falcon's basic design proved to be adaptable to both the more advanced air-to-air weapons now in use or planned, and to a wide variety of air-to-ground weaponry. It has retained the M-61A1 Vulcan 20MM cannon with double ended linkless feed system having a capacity of 500 rounds and a steady-state firing rate of 6,000 rounds per minute. The gun is installed aft of the cockpit and avionics bays to avoid imposing the severe environmental conditions (shock, gases, heat) on the pilot, avionics, and engine inlet. It's position above the forebody strake effectively prevents ingestion of gun gases, which might cause compressor stalls. Provisions for external stores include nine store stations incorporating launchers, and pylons to attach missiles, fuel tanks, bombs, electronic countermeasures pods, dispensers, or even the unthinkable. In it's present form, the F-16 is one of the most potent air-to-air combat fighters ever flown. It's small size and smokeless engine makes it a tough target to acquire visually, and it's acceleration and turning ability makes it a slippery target. The F-16's intergrated fire control system tracks the target flight path parameters and presents the information to the pilot on the Head-Up-Display (HUD) in his gunsight. Also displayed on the HUD are his airspeed and altitude, and how many Gs he is pulling. One of the primary criticisms of the F-16 has been it's lack of a Beyond Visual Range capability. This will be solved with the installation of the new APG-66 Westinghouse Radar and the operational debut of the AMRAAM (Advanced Medium Range Air-to-Air Missile). For it's small size, the F-16 packs a potent punch in the air-to-ground role. With comparable loads, it has more than twice the range of the F-4 Phantom. Payloads of 12,000 lb. can be carried with full internal fuel. Loading and release of stores is facilitated by the F-16's integrated, digital stores management system. The system permits precise pilot control of impact pattern and spacing for each type of weapon. The F-16's radar ground mapping modes provide pinpoint target location, and allows visual or blind bombing. The APG-66 radar operates in X band to minimize atmospheric degradation and uses low and medium-pulse Doppler techniques to allow clutter-free look-down capability.

Switches on the throttle, side-stick controller, or radar control panel allow the pilot to change radar modes quickly and with head up, which means he does not have to take his eyes off the target as he maneuvers into firing position and selects his weapons. The mode options include: **Search volume,** which controls range, azimuth, and raster; **Missile mode,** which provides fully dynamic launch parameters; **Air-to-air gunnery modes** which provide snapshoot no-lock-on, gunnery solutions based on bullet trajectory or utilizing the lead-computing gunsight for fully locked-on firing solutions. Finally, there is a **Dogfight mode** which overrides all other modes and provides boresight or slewable search. In this mode, the radar automatically searches and locks onto targets out to 10 nautical miles. After lock-on, full tracking parameters are displayed automatically on the HUD. All this is accomplished with one switch on the throttle.

F-16B of the 388th TFW prepares to taxi during Red Flag 80-2 at Nellis AFB, Nevada. (SSGT Roy Chismar)

F-16B of the 3246th Test Wing carries inert Mk 82 Snakeye high drag bombs over the Gulf of Mexico near Eglin AFB, Florida. (General Dynamics)

Over Twice the Range of the F-4 – With the Same Payload

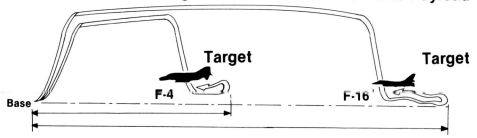

Armaments

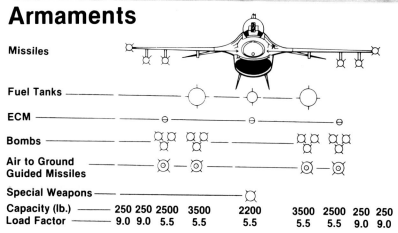

	Missiles	Fuel Tanks	ECM	Bombs	Air to Ground Guided Missiles	Special Weapons

Capacity (lb.)	250	250	2500	3500	2200	3500	2500	250	250
Load Factor	9.0	9.0	5.5	5.5	5.5	5.5	5.5	9.0	9.0

(Below) Pave Penny Laser seeker pod as mounted on 388th TFW F-16A during operational test and evaluation (SSGT Roy Chismar)

(Above) 500 rounds of ammunition were test fired from the General Electric GPU-5/A (GEPOD-30) four barrel 30MM gun mounted in a pod on the centerline of an F-16A fixed to a test stand at Fort Worth. Gun was fired by remote control. Flight tests with the pod are scheduled for 1984. (General Dynamics)

(Below) Large black drum holds the 500 rounds of ammunition for the 20MM Vulcan cannon. (SSGT Roy Chismar)

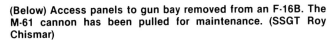

(Below) Access panels to gun bay removed from an F-16B. The M-61 cannon has been pulled for maintenance. (SSGT Roy Chismar)

F-16 Accuracy is Unexcelled

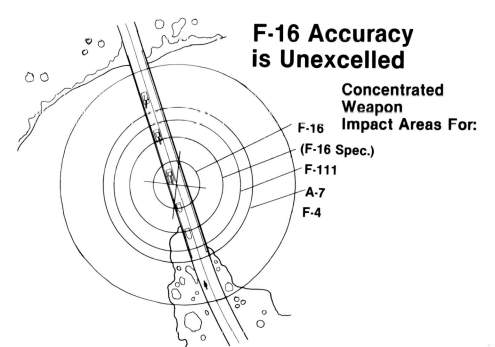

Concentrated Weapon Impact Areas For:

- F-16
- (F-16 Spec.)
- F-111
- A-7
- F-4

(Above and below) F-16A-5-CF of the 3246th Test Wing, Eglin AFB, Florida during compatibility testing of the latest air-to-ground munitions, October, 1981. (Norman E. Taylor)

If you liked *The Electric Jet* ...
...you'll LOVE Lou Drendel's
SR-71 Blackbird in Action